Organic Chemistry Laboratory Manual

THIRD EDITION

Pavia | Lampman | Kriz | Engel

Edited by
Karla Radke | Gary Stolzenberg

CENGAGE
Learning™

Australia • Brazil • Japan • Korea • Mexico • Singapore • Spain • United Kingdom • United States

CENGAGE
Learning™

Organic Chemistry Laboratory Manual
Third Edition

Pavia | Lampman | Kriz | Engel
Edited by Karla Radke | Gary Stolzenberg

Executive Editor:
Michael Stranz

Custom Editor:
Robert Tessman

Custom Production Editor:
Jennifer Flinchpaugh

Project Coordinators:
Lisa Donahue, Peg Hagar

Senior Pre-Press Specialist:
Kathy Paxton

Production Supervisor-Labs:
Melanie Evans

Rights and Permissions Specialist:
Kalina Ingham Hintz

Marketing Specialist:
Sara Mercurio

Cover Images:
© Getty Images

Library of Congress Control Number: 2009924503

For product information and technology assistance, contact us at
Cengage Learning Customer & Sales Support, 1-800-354-9706

For permission to use material from this text or product,
submit all requests online at **cengage.com/permissions**
Further permissions questions can be emailed to
permissionrequest@cengage.com

ISBN-13: 978-1-4240-6408-3

ISBN-10: 1-4240-6408-2

Cengage Learning
5191 Natorp Boulevard
Mason, OH 45040
USA

Cengage Learning is a leading provider of customized learning solutions with office locations around the globe, including Singapore, the United Kingdom, Australia, Mexico, Brazil, and Japan. Locate your local office at:
international.cengage.com/region

Cengage Learning products are represented in Canada by Nelson Education, Ltd.

Visit Signature Labs online at **signaturelabs.com**

Visit our corporate website at **cengage.com**

Printed in the United States of America

Contents

TLC Analysis of Analgesic Drugs

Prepared by Donald L. Pavia, Gary M. Lampman and George S. Kriz, Western Washington University, and Richard Engel, Edmonds Community College

INTRODUCTION

In this experiment, thin-layer chromatography (TLC) will be used to determine the composition of various over-the-counter analgesics. If the instructor chooses, you may also be required to identify the components and actual identity (trade name) of an unknown analgesic. You will be given two commercially prepared TLC plates with a flexible backing and a silica gel coating with a fluorescent indicator. On the first TLC plate, a reference plate, you will spot four standard compounds often used in analgesic formulations. In addition, a standard reference mixture containing four of these same compounds will also be spotted. On the second plate (the sample plate) you will spot several commercial analgesic preparations in order to determine their composition. At your instructor's option, one or more of these may be an unknown.

Reference Plate One		Sample Plate
Acetaminophen	(Ac)	Four commercial preparations (or
Aspirin	(Asp)	unknowns) plus the reference
Caffeine	(Cf)	mixture
Salicylamide	(Sal)	
Reference mixture 1	(Ref-1)	

The standard compounds will be all available as solutions of 1 g of each dissolved in 20 mL of a 50:50 mixture of methylene chloride and ethanol. The purpose of the first reference plate is to determine the order of elution (R_f values) of the known substances and to index the standard reference mixture. On the sample plate, the standard reference mixture will be spotted, along with several solutions that have been prepared from commercial analgesic tablets.

Two methods of visualization will be used to observe the positions of the spots on the developed TLC plates. First, the plates will be observed while under illumination from a short-wavelength ultraviolet (UV) lamp. This is done best in a darkened room or in a fume hood that has been darkened by taping butcher paper or aluminum foil over the lowered glass cover. Under these conditions, some of the spots will appear as dark areas on the plate, while others will fluoresce brightly. This difference in appearance under UV illumination will help to distinguish the substances from one another. You will find it convenient to outline very lightly in *pencil* the spots observed and to place a small X inside those spots that fluoresce. For a second means of visualization, iodine vapor will be used. Not all the spots will become visible when treated with iodine, but some will develop yellow, tan, or deep brown colors. The differences in the behaviors of the various spots with iodine can be used to further differentiate among them.

It is possible to use several developing solvents for this experiment, but ethyl acetate with 0.5% glacial acetic acid added is preferred. The small amount of glacial acetic acid supplies protons and suppresses ionization of aspirin, ibuprofen, naproxen sodium and ketoprofen, allowing them to travel upward on the plates in their protonated form. Without the acid, these compounds do not move.

In some analgesics, you may find ingredients besides the five mentioned previously. Some include an antihistamine and some a mild sedative. For instance, Midol contains *N*-cinnamylephedrine (cinnamedrine), an antihistamine, while Excedrin PM contains the sedative methapyrilene hydrochloride. Cope contains the related sedative methapyrilene fumarate. Some tablets may be colored with a chemical dye.

SPECIAL INSTRUCTIONS

You must examine the developed plates under ultraviolet light first. After comparisons of *all* plates have been made with UV light, iodine vapor can be used. The iodine permanently affects some of the spots, making it impossible to go back and repeat the UV visualization. Take special care to notice those substances that have similar R_f values; these spots each have a different appearance when viewed under UV illumination, or a different staining color with iodine, allowing you to distinguish among them.

Aspirin presents some special problems since it is present in a large amount in many of the analgesics and since it hydrolyzes easily. For these reasons, the aspirin spots often show excessive tailing.

WASTE DISPOSAL

Dispose of all development solvent in the container for organic solvents. The micropipets used for spotting the solution should be placed in a broken-glass container.

PROCEDURE

Initial Preparations

You will need at least 12 capillary micropipets to spot the plates. A common error is to pull the center section out too far when making these pipets, with the result that too little sample is applied to the plate. If this happens, you won't see *any* spots. Follow the directions carefully.

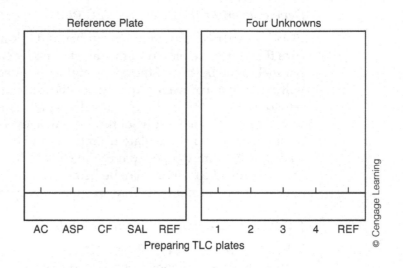

After preparing the micropipets, obtain two (silica) TLC plates. These plates have a flexible backing, but they should not be bent excessively. Handle them carefully or the adsorbent may flake off. Also, you should handle them only by the edges; the surface should not be touched. Using a lead pencil (not a pen), *lightly* draw a line across the plates (short dimension) about 1 cm from the bottom. Using a ruler, move its index about 0.6 cm in from the edge of the plate and lightly mark off five 1-cm intervals on the line (see figure). These are the points at which the samples will be spotted.

Spotting the Reference Plate

On the first plate (starting from left to right), spot acetaminophen, then aspirin, caffeine, and salicylamide. This order is alphabetic and should avoid any further confusion among spots. The standard reference mixture (Ref) is spotted in the last position. It is important that the spots be made as small as possible, but not too small. With too much sample, the spots will tail and will overlap one another after development. With too little sample, no spots will be observed after development. The optimum applied spot should be about 1–2 mm (1/16 in.) in diameter. If scrap pieces of the TLC plates are available, it would be a good idea to practice spotting on these before preparing the actual sample plates.

Preparing the Development Chamber

When the reference plate (or plates) have been spotted, obtain a wide-mouthed screwcap jar (or other suitable container) for use as a development chamber.

Obtain a small amount of the development solvent (0.5% glacial acetic acid in ethyl acetate). Your instructor should prepare this mixture; it contains such a small amount of acetic acid that small individual portions are difficult to prepare. Fill the chamber with the development solvent to a depth of about 0.5–0.7 cm. Recall that the solvent level must not be above the spots on the plate or the samples will dissolve off the plate into the reservoir instead of developing.

Development of the Reference TLC Plate

Place the spotted plate in the chamber and allow the spots to develop. Be sure the plates are placed in the developing jar so that their bottom edge is parallel to the bottom of the jar (straight, not tilted); if not, the solvent front will not advance evenly, increasing the difficulty of making good comparisons. Do *NOT* move the development chamber while your plate is developing! When the solvent has risen to a level about 0.5 cm from the top of the plate, remove the plate from the chamber (in the hood) and, using a lead pencil, mark the position of the solvent front. Set the plate on a piece of paper towel to dry. It may be helpful to place a small object under one end to allow optimum air flow around the drying plate.

UV Visualization of the Reference Plate

When the plate is dry, observe it under a short-wavelength UV lamp, preferably in a darkened hood or a darkened room. Lightly outline all of the observed spots with a pencil. Carefully notice any differences in behavior between the spotted substances. Several compounds have similar R_f values, but the spots may have a different appearance under UV illumination or iodine staining. Before proceeding, make a sketch of the plate in your notebook and note the differences in appearance that you observed. Using a ruler marked in millimeters, measure the distance that each spot has traveled relative to the solvent front. Calculate R_f values for each spot.

Spot the over-the-counter analgesic extracts on the sample plate. At the fifth position, spot the standard reference solution (Ref). Develop the plate in 0.5% glacial acetic acid-ethyl acetate as before. Observe the plate under UV illumination and mark the visible spots as you did for the first plate. Sketch the plate in your notebook and record your conclusions about the contents of each over-the-counter analgesic. This can be done by directly comparing your plate to the reference plate—they can all be placed under the UV light at the same time.

Iodine Analysis

Do not perform this step until UV comparisons of all the plates are complete. When ready, place the plates in a jar containing a few iodine crystals, cap the jar, and warm it gently with your hands until the spots begin to appear. Notice which spots become visible and note their relative colors. You can directly compare colors of the reference spots to those on the unknown plate. Remove the plates from the jar and record your observations in your notebook.

QUESTIONS

1. What happens if the spots are made too large when preparing a TLC plate for development?
2. What happens if the spots are made too small when preparing a TLC plate for development?
3. Why must the spots be above the level of the development solvent in the developing chamber?

4. What would happen if the spotting line and positions were marked on the plate with a ballpoint pen?

5. Is it possible to distinguish two spots that have the same R_f value, but represent different compounds? Give two different methods.

6. Name some advantages of using acetaminophen (Tylenol) instead of aspirin as an analgesic.

Isolation of Casein and Lactose from Milk

Prepared by Donald L. Pavia, Gary M. Lampman and George S. Kriz, Western Washington University, and Richard Engel, Edmonds Community College

INTRODUCTION

In this experiment, you will isolate several of the chemical substances found in milk. First, you will isolate a phosphorus-containing protein, casein. The remaining milk mixture will then be used as a source of a sugar, α-lactose. Fats, which are present in whole milk, are not isolated in this experiment because powdered nonfat milk is used.

Here is the procedure you will follow. First, the casein is precipitated by warming the powdered milk and adding dilute acetic acid. It is important that the heating not be excessive or the acid too strong, because these conditions also hydrolyze lactose into its components, glucose and galactose. After the casein has been removed, the excess acetic acid is neutralized with calcium carbonate, and the solution is heated to its boiling point to precipitate the initially soluble protein, albumin. The liquid containing the lactose is poured away from the albumin. Alcohol is added to the solution, and any remaining protein is removed by centrifugation. α-Lactose crystallizes on cooling.

Lactose is an example of a disaccharide. It is made up of two sugar molecules: galactose and glucose. In the preceding structures, the galactose portion is on the left and glucose is on the right. Galactose is bonded through an acetal linkage to glucose.

Notice that the glucose portion can exist in one of two isomeric hemiacetal structures: α-lactose and β-lactose. Glucose can also exist in a free aldehyde form. This aldehyde form (open form) is an intermediate in the equilibration (interconversion) of α- and β-lactose. Very little of this free aldehyde form exists in the equilibrium mixture. The isomeric α- and β-lactose are distereomers because they differ in the configuration at one carbon atom, called the anomeric carbon atom.

The sugar α-lactose is easily obtainable by crystallization from a water-ethanol mixture at room temperature. On the other hand, β-lactose must be obtained by a more difficult process, which involves crystallization

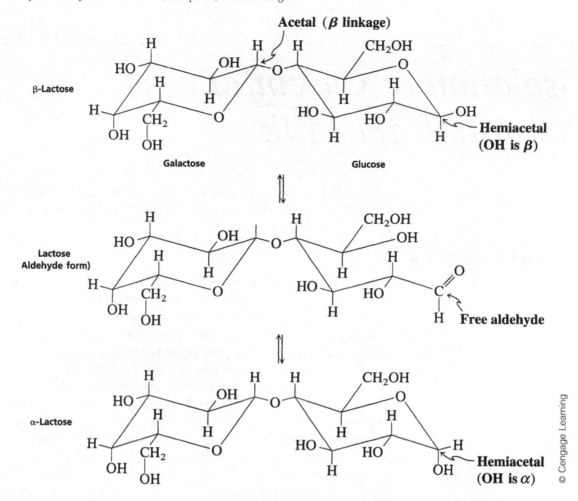

from a concentrated solution of lactose at temperatures about 93.5°C. In the present experiment, α-lactose is isolated because the experimental procedure is easier.

PROCEDURE: ISOLATION OF CASEIN FROM MILK

Precipitation of Casein

Place 4.0 g of powdered milk and 25 mL of water into a 150-mL beaker. Heat the mixture in a water bath to 40°C. Check the temperature of the milk solution with a thermometer. Place 2.0 mL of dilute acetic acid solution[1] in a small flask for temporary storage. When the mixture has reached 40°C, add the dilute acetic acid dropwise to the warm milk. After every 5 drops, stir the mixture gently using a glass stirring rod. Using a stirring rod, push the casein up onto the side of the beaker so that most of the liquid drains from the solid. Then transfer the congealed casein to

---

[1]The laboratory instructor should prepare a large batch for the class in the ratio of 2 mL glacial acetic acid to 20 mL of water.

another small beaker in portions. If any liquid separates from the casein in the small beaker, use a Pasteur pipet to transfer the liquid back into the reaction mixture. Continue to add dropwise the remainder of the 2.0 mL of dilute acetic acid to the milk mixture in the beaker to precipitate the casein fully. Remove as much of the casein as possible and transfer it to the small beaker. Avoid adding an excess of acetic acid to the milk solution, as this will cause the lactose in the milk to hydrolyze into glucose and galactose.

When you have removed most of the casein from the milk solution, add 0.2 g of calcium carbonate to the milk in the beaker. Stir the mixture for a few minutes. Use this mixture as soon as possible during the laboratory period. This beaker contains lactose and albumins.

PROCEDURE: ISOLATION OF LACTOSE FROM MILK

Precipitation of Albumins

Heat the mixture directly on a hot plate in the 150-mL beaker to about 75°C for about 5 minutes. This heating operation results in a nearly complete separation of the albumins from the solution. Decant the liquid in the beaker away from the solid into a clean centrifuge tube. You may need to hold the solid with a spatula while transferring the liquid. Press the albumins with a spatula to remove as much liquid as possible and pour the liquid into the centrifuge tube. When the liquid has cooled to about room temperature, centrifuge the contents of the tube for 2–3 minutes. Be sure to place another tube in the centrifuge to balance the unit. Following centrifugation, decant the liquid away from the solid into a beaker and save it for use in the next section (Precipitation of Lactose).

Precipitation of Lactose

Add 20 mL of 95% ethanol to the beaker containing the centrifuged and decanted liquid. Solids will precipitate. Heat this mixture to about 60°C, placing it directly on the hotplate, to dissolve some of the solid. Pour the *hot* liquid into centrifuge tubes and centrifuge the hot solution as soon as possible before the solution cools appreciably. Centrifuge the mixture for 2–3 minutes. Be sure to place another tube in the centrifuge to balance the unit. It is important to centrifuge this mixture while it is warm to prevent premature crystallization of the lactose. A considerable quantity of solid forms in the bottom of the centrifuge tube. This solid is not lactose.

Remove the warm supernatant liquid from the tube using a Pasteur pipet and transfer the liquid to a small Erlenmeyer flask and cap with a plug. Discard the solid remaining in the centrifuge tube. Plug the flask with a paper towel and allow the lactose to crystallize for one week. Granular crystals will form during this time.

Isolation of Lactose

Collect the lactose by vacuum filtration on a Buchner funnel. Use about 3 mL of 95% ethanol to aid the transfer and to wash the product. α-Lactose crystallizes with one water of hydration, $C_{12}H_{22}O_{11} \cdot H_2O$. Weigh the product after it is thoroughly dry. Calculate the weight percent of the lactose isolated from the powdered milk.

QUESTIONS

1. A student decided to determine the optical rotation of mucic acid. What should be expected as a value? Why?

2. Draw a mechanism for the acid-catalyzed hydrolysis of the acetal bond in lactose.

3. β-Lactose is present to a larger extent in an aqueous solution when the solution is at equilibrium. Why is this to be expected?

4. Very little of the free aldehyde form is present in an equilibrium mixture of lactose. However, a positive test is obtained with Benedict's reagent. Explain.

5. Using a flowchart, outline a separation scheme for isolating casein, albumin, and lactose from milk.

Acetaminophen

Prepared by Donald L. Pavia, Gary M. Lampman and George S. Kriz, Western Washington University, and Richard Engel, Edmonds Community College

INTRODUCTION

Preparation of acetaminophen involves treating an amine with an acid anhydride to form an amide. In this case, *p*-aminophenol, the amine, is treated with acetic anhydride to form acetaminophen (*p*-acetamidophenol), the amide.

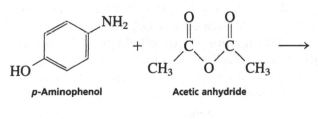

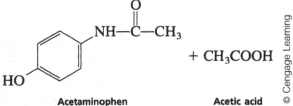

The crude solid acetaminophen contains dark impurities carried along with the *p*-aminophenol starting material. These impurities, which are dyes of unknown structure, are formed from oxidation of the starting phenol. While the amount of the dye impurity is small, it is intense enough to impart color to the crude acetaminophen. Most of the colored impurity is destroyed by heating the crude product with sodium dithionite (sodium hydrosulfite $Na_2S_2O_4$). The dithionite reduces double bonds in the colored dye to produce colorless substances.

The decolorized acetaminophen is collected on a Büchner funnel. It is further purified by recrystallization from a mixture of methanol and water.

SPECIAL INSTRUCTIONS

Acetic anhydride can cause irritation of tissue, especially in nasal passages. Avoid breathing the vapor and avoid contact with skin and eyes. *p*-Aminophenol is a skin irritant and is toxic.

PROCEDURE

Reaction Mixture

Weigh about 1.5 g of *p*-aminophenol, and place this in a 50-mL Erlenmeyer flask. Using a graduated cylinder, add 4.5 mL of water and 1.7 mL of acetic anhydride. Place a magnetic stir bar in the flask.

Heating

Heat the reaction mixture, with stirring, directly on a hotplate using a thermometer to monitor the internal temperature (about 100°C). After the solid has dissolved (it may dissolve, precipitate, and redissolve), heat the mixture for an additional 10 minutes at about 100°C to complete the reaction.

Isolation of Crude Acetominophen

Remove the flask from the hotplate and allow the flask to cool to room temperature. If crystallization has not occurred, scratch the inside of the flask with a glass stirring rod to initiate crystallization. Cool the mixture thoroughly in an ice bath for 15 minutes and collect the crystals by vacuum filtration on a small Büchner funnel. Rinse the flask with about 5 mL of ice water and transfer this mixture to the Büchner funnel. Wash the crystals on the funnel with two additional 5 mL portions of ice water. Dry the crystals for 10 minutes by allowing air to be drawn through them while they remain on the Büchner funnel. During this drying period, break up any large clumps of crystals with a spatula. Weigh the crude product and set aside a small sample for a melting point determination and a color comparison after the next step. Calculate the percentage yield of crude acetaminophen. Record the appearance of the crystals in your notebook.

Recrystallization of Acetaminophen

Place the crude acetaminophen and 2.0 g sodium dithionite in a 50-mL Erlenmeyer flask. Recrystallize the material from a solvent mixture composed of 50% water and 50% methanol by volume. The solubility of acetaminophen in this hot (nearly boiling) solvent is about 1 g/5 mL. Add small portions of hot solvent until the solid dissolves. When dissolved, allow the mixture to cool slowly to room temperature.

When the mixture has cooled to room temperature, place the flask in an ice bath for at least 10 minutes. If necessary, induce crystallization by scratching the inside of the flask with a glass stirring rod. Because acetaminophen may crystallize *slowly* from the solvent, it is necessary to cool the flask in an ice bath for the 10-minute period. Collect the crystals using a Büchner funnel. Dry the crystals for 5–10 minutes by allowing air to be drawn through them while they remain on the Büchner funnel.

Yield Calculation and Melting Point Determination

Weigh the crystallized acetaminophen and calculate the percentage yield. This calculation should be based on the original amount of *p*-aminophenol used at the beginning of this procedure. Determine the melting point of the product. Compare the melting point of this final product with that of the crude acetaminophen. Also compare the colors of the crude and purified acetaminophen.

QUESTIONS

1. During the crystallization of acetaminophen, why was the mixture cooled in an ice bath?

2. In the reaction between *p*-aminophenol and acetic anhydride to form acetaminophen, 4.5 mL of water was added. What was the purpose of the water?

3. Why should you use a minimum amount of water to rinse the flask while transferring the purified acetaminophen to the Büchner funnel?

4. If 1.30 g of *p*-aminophenol is allowed to react with excess acetic anhydride, what is the theoretical yield of acetaminophen in moles? In grams? Show your work!

5. Give two reasons why the crude product in most reactions is not pure.

6. Phenacetin has the structure shown. Write an equation for its preparation starting from 4-ethoxyaniline.

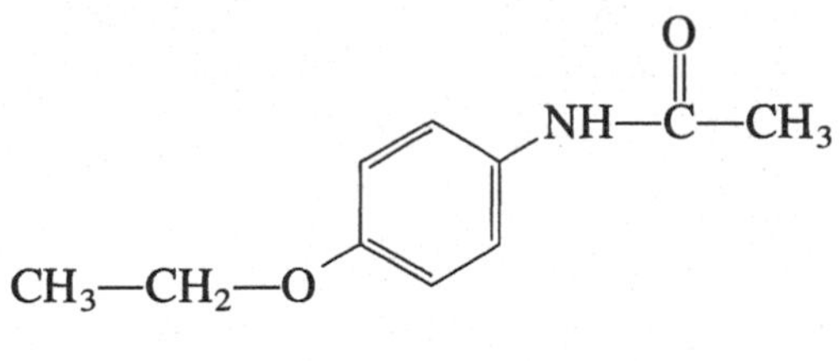

© Cengage Learning

Isopentyl Acetate (Banana Oil)

Prepared by Donald L. Pavia, Gary M. Lampman and George S. Kriz, Western Washington University, and Richard Engel, Edmonds Community College

This experiment involves the preparation of an ester, isopentyl acetate. This ester is often referred to as banana oil, since it has the familiar odor of this fruit.

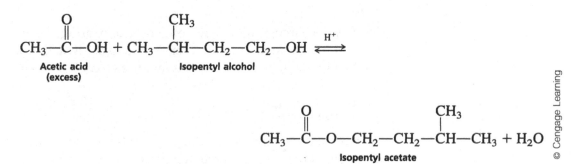

Isopentyl acetate is prepared by the direct esterification of acetic acid with isopentyl alcohol. Since the equilibrium does not favor the formation of the ester, it must be shifted to the right, in favor of the product, by using an excess of one of the starting materials. Acetic acid is used in excess because it is less expensive than isopentyl alcohol and more easily removed from the reaction mixture.

In the isolation procedure, much of the excess acetic acid and the remaining isopentyl alcohol are removed by extraction with sodium bicarbonate and water. After drying with anhydrous sodium sulfate, the ester is purified by distillation.

SPECIAL INSTRUCTIONS

Be careful when dispensing sulfuric and glacial acetic acids. They are very corrosive and will attack your skin if you make contact with them. If you get one of these acids on your skin, wash the affected area with copious quantities of running water for 10–15 minutes.

PROCEDURE

Apparatus

Assemble a reflux apparatus, using a 25-mL round-bottom flask and a water-cooled condenser. Use a heating mantle to heat.

Reaction Mixture

Weigh (tare) an empty 10-mL graduated cylinder and record its weight. Place approximately 5.0 mL of isopentyl alcohol in the graduated cylinder and reweigh it to determine the weight of alcohol. Disconnect the round-bottom flask from the reflux apparatus and transfer the alcohol into it. Do not clean or wash the graduated cylinder. Using the same graduated cylinder, measure approximately 7.0 mL of glacial acetic acid and add it to the alcohol already in the flask. Using a calibrated Pasteur pipet, add 1 mL of concentrated sulfuric acid, mixing *immediately* (swirl), to the reaction mixture contained in the flask. Add a boiling stone and reconnect the flask.

Reflux

Start water circulating in the condenser and bring the mixture to a boil. Continue heating under reflux for 75 minutes. Then, disconnect or remove the heating source and allow the mixture to cool to room temperature.

Extractions

Disassemble the apparatus and transfer the reaction mixture to a separatory funnel placed in a ring that is attached to a ring stand. Be sure that the stopcock is closed and, using a funnel, pour the mixture into the top of the separatory funnel. Also be careful to avoid transferring the boiling stone. Add 10 mL of ice water, stopper the funnel, and mix the phases by careful shaking and venting. Allow the phases to separate and then unstopper the funnel and drain the lower aqueous layer through the stopcock into a beaker or other suitable container. Next, extract the organic layer with 5 mL of saturated aqueous sodium bicarbonate just as you did previously with water. Extract the organic layer once again, this time with 5 mL of saturated aqueous sodium chloride.

Drying

Transfer the crude ester to a clean, dry 25-mL round-bottom flask with a plug and dry with anhydrous sodium sulfate. Cork the mixture and allow it to stand until the next class period.

Distillation

Take the mass of your sample by decanting the liquid into a clean, pre-weighed flask. Assemble a distillation apparatus using your smallest round-bottom flask to distill from. Use a heating mantle to heat. Pre-weigh (tare) and use another small round-bottom flask, or an Erlenmeyer flask, to collect the product. Immerse the collection flask in a beaker of ice to ensure condensation and to reduce odors. You should look up the boiling point of your expected product in a handbook so you will know what to expect. Continue distillation until only one or two drops of liquid remain in the distilling flask. Record the observed boiling point *range* in your notebook.

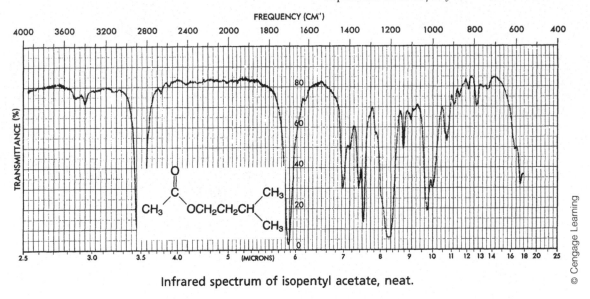

Infrared spectrum of isopentyl acetate, neat.

© Cengage Learning

Yield Determination

Weigh the product and calculate the percentage yield of the ester.

QUESTIONS

1. One method of favoring the formation of an ester is to add excess acetic acid. Suggest another method, involving the right-hand side of the equation, that will favor the formation of the ester.

2. Why is the mixture extracted with sodium bicarbonate? Give a chemical equation and explain its relevance.

3. Why are gas bubbles observed when the mixture is extracted with sodium bicarbonate?

4. Which starting material is the limiting reagent in this procedure? Which reagent is used in excess? How great is the molar excess (how many times greater)?

5. Outline a separation scheme for isolating pure isopentyl acetate from the reaction mixture.

6. Interpret the principal absorption bands in the infrared spectrum of isopentyl acetate or, if you did not determine the infrared spectrum of your ester, do this for the spectrum of isopentyl acetate shown above.

7. Write a mechanism for the acid-catalyzed esterification of acetic acid with isopentyl alcohol.

8. Why is glacial acetic acid designated as "glacial"?

Gas Chromatographic Analysis of Isopentyl Acetate

Prepared by the Department of Chemistry and Molecular Biology,
North Dakota State University

INTRODUCTION

In this experiment you will use the technique of gas chromatography to analyze the purity of synthetic isopentyl acetate. Different boiling fractions from the distillation of your product will be used. The extent of any impurities or starting materials present will be determined.

You will be analyzing samples of the isopentyl acetate you prepared in the previous lab. In order to examine the purity of your distilled product, two fractions will be collected. In one receiver, you should collect the fraction boiling between 120 and 132°C. In a separate flask, collect the fraction boiling between 134 and 143°C. These will be analyzed by GC. You may be asked to collect more than two fractions, in which case the boiling ranges will be given to you by your lab instructor. Or, some groups may be asked to carry out a simple distillation while others will carry out a fractional distillation with a special vigreux distillation column.

PROCEDURE

Your product from the previous experiment will be distilled according to instructions from your lab TA. A standard GC spectrum of isopentyl acetate and isopentyl alcohol will be made available by your instructor. These are to be used to compare with your product spectrum. Because the special GC syringes are expensive and very delicate, your instructor will be making the injections for you. Samples of your product fractions should be prepared. In a vial dissolve 1–2 drops of your product in about 1 mL of ethanol. Make a sample of the product pool before distillation and the fractions after distillation. Label the vials accordingly. Inject one sample and wait for the chromatogram to be recorded. Inject the other sample and obtain its chromatogram. Compare these spectra to the standard ones provided. Identify which peak belongs to the starting isopentyl alcohol and which peak belongs to the product. Determine which sample is more pure. If there are any other peaks, make a guess as to its identity. Be sure to record the retention times and determine the ratio of compounds in the chromatogram. Compare the purity of the distilled samples to the undistilled "crude" product. If the class is asked to carry out the distillations differently, compare and contrast your results with the other method. Your report should include a copy of the GC traces.

QUESTIONS

1. If you were to make the ester from 1-pentanol and acetic acid, would the retention time of the product be longer or shorter than for isopentyl acetate? Explain.

2. What are two advantages for using gas chromatography over other separation methods?

Isolation of Caffeine from Coffee

Prepared by Donald L. Pavia, Gary M. Lampman and George S. Kriz, Western Washington University, and Richard Engel, North Seattle Community College; and Dr. Sanku Mallik, North Dakota State University

INTRODUCTION

The origins of coffee and tea as beverages are so old that they are lost in legend. Coffee is said to have been discovered by an Abyssinian goatherder who noticed an unusual friskiness in his goats when they consumed a certain little plant with red berries. He decided to try the berries himself and discovered coffee. The Arabs soon cultivated the coffee plant, and one of the earliest descriptions of its use is found in an Arabian medical book circa A.D. 900. The great systematic botanist Linnaeus named the tree *Coffea arabica.*

One legend of the discovery of tea—from the Orient, as you might expect—attributes the discovery to Daruma, the founder of Zen. Legend has it that he inadvertently fell asleep one day during his customary meditations. To be assured that this indiscretion would not recur, he cut off both eyelids. Where they fell to the ground, a new plant took root that had the power to keep a person awake. Although some experts assert that the medical use of tea was reported as early as 2737 B.C. in the pharmacopeia of Shen Nung, an emperor of China, the first indisputable reference is from the Chinese dictionary of Kuo P'o, which appeared in A.D. 350. The non-medical, or popular, use of tea appears to have spread slowly. Not until about A.D. 700 was tea widely cultivated in China. Tea is native to upper Indochina and upper India, so it must have been cultivated in these places before its introduction to China. Linnaeus named the tea shrub *Thea sinensis;* however, tea is more properly a relative of the camellia, and botanists have renamed it *Camellia thea.*

The active ingredient that makes tea and coffee valuable to humans is **caffeine.** Caffeine is an **alkaloid,** a class of naturally occurring compounds containing nitrogen and having the properties of an organic amine base (alkaline, hence, *alkaloid).* Tea and coffee are not the only plant sources of caffeine. Others include kola nuts, maté leaves, guarana seeds, and in small amount, cocoa beans. The pure alkaloid was first isolated from coffee in 1821 by the French chemist Pierre Jean Robiquet.

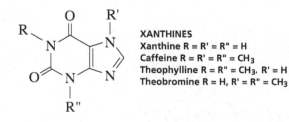

XANTHINES
Xanthine R = R' = R" = H
Caffeine R = R' = R" = CH₃
Theophylline R = R" = CH₃, R' = H
Theobromine R = H, R' = R" = CH₃

© Cengage Learning

Caffeine belongs to a family of naturally occurring compounds called **xanthines.** The xanthines, in the form of their plant progenitors, are possibly the oldest known stimulants. They all, to various extents, stimulate the central nervous system and the skeletal muscles. This stimulation results in an increased alertness, the ability to put off sleep, and an increased capacity for thinking. Caffeine is the most powerful xanthine in this respect. It is the main ingredient of the popular No-Doz keep-alert tablets. Although caffeine has a powerful effect on the central nervous system, not all xanthines are as effective. Thus, theobromine, the xanthine found in cocoa, has fewer central nervous system effects. It is, however, a strong **diuretic** (induces urination) and is useful to doctors in treating patients with severe water-retention problems. Theophylline, a second xanthine found in tea, also has fewer central nervous system effects but is a strong **myocardial** (heart muscle) stimulant; it **dilates** (relaxes) the coronary artery that supplies blood to the heart. Its most important use is in the treatment of bronchial asthma because it has the properties of a **bronchodilator** (relaxes the bronchioles of the lungs). Because it is also a **vasodilator** (relaxes blood vessels), it is often used in treating hypertensive headaches. It is also used to alleviate and to reduce the frequency of attacks of **angina pectoris** (severe chest pain). In addition, it is a more powerful diuretic than theobromine.

One can develop both a tolerance for the xanthines and a dependence on them, particularly caffeine. The dependence is real, and a heavy user (>5 cups of coffee per day) will experience lethargy, headache, and perhaps nausea after about 18 hours of abstinence. An excessive intake of caffeine may lead to restlessness, irritability, insomnia, and muscular tremor. Caffeine can be toxic, but to achieve a lethal dose of caffeine, one would have to drink about 100 cups of coffee over a relatively short period.

Caffeine is a natural constituent of coffee, tea, and kola nuts *(Kola nitida)*. Theophylline is found as a minor constituent of tea. The chief constituent of cocoa is theobromine. The amount of caffeine in tea varies from 2% to 5%. In one analysis of black tea, the following compounds were found: caffeine, 2.5%; theobromine, 0.17%; theophylline, 0.013%; adenine, 0.014%; and guanine and xanthine, traces. Coffee beans can contain up to 5% by weight of caffeine, and cocoa contains around 5% theobromine. Commercial cola is a beverage based on a kola nut extract. We cannot easily get kola nuts in this country, but we can get the ubiquitous commercial extract as a syrup. The syrup can be converted into "cola." The syrup contains caffeine, tannins, pigments, and sugar. Phosphoric acid is added, and caramel is added to give the syrup a deep color. The final drink is prepared by adding water and carbon dioxide under pressure to give the bubbly mixture. Before decaffeination, the Food and Drug Administration required a "cola" to contain some caffeine (about 0.2 mg per ounce). In 1990, when new nutrition labels were adopted, this requirement was dropped. The Food and Drug Administration currently requires that a "cola" contain *some* caffeine but limits this amount to a maximum of 5 milligrams per ounce. To achieve a regulated level of caffeine, most manufacturers remove all caffeine from the kola extract and then re-add the correct amount to the syrup. The caffeine content of various beverages is listed in the accompanying table.

With the recent popularity of gourmet coffee beans and espresso stands, it is interesting to consider the caffeine content of these specialty beverages. Gourmet coffee certainly has more flavor than the typical ground coffee you may find on any grocery store shelf, and the concentration of brewed gourmet coffee tends to be higher than ordinary drip-grind coffee. Brewed gourmet coffee probably contains something on the order of 20–25 mg of caffeine per ounce of liquid. Espresso coffee is a very concentrated, dark-brewed coffee. Although the darker roasted beans used for espresso actually contain less caffeine per gram than regularly roasted beans, the method of preparing espresso (extraction using pressurized steam) is more efficient, and a higher percentage of the total caffeine in the beans is extracted. The caffeine content per ounce of liquid, therefore, is substantially higher than in most brewed coffees. The serving size for espresso coffee, however, is much smaller than for ordinary coffee (about 1.5–2 oz per serving), so the total caffeine available in a serving of espresso turns out to be about the same as in a serving of ordinary coffee.

Amount of caffeine (mg/oz) found in beverages

Brewed coffee	12–30	Tea	4–20
Instant coffee	8–20	Cocoa (but 20 mg/oz theobromine)	0.5–2
Espresso (1 serving = 1.5–2 oz)	50–70	Coca-Cola®	3.75
Decaffeinated coffee	0.4–1.0		

Note: The average cup of coffee or tea contains about 5–7 oz of liquid. The average bottle of cola contains about 12 oz of liquid.

Because of the central nervous system effects from caffeine, many people prefer **decaffeinated** coffee. The caffeine is removed from coffee by extracting the whole beans with an organic solvent. Then the solvent is drained off, and the beans are steamed to remove any residual solvent. The beans are dried and roasted to bring out the flavor. Decaffeination reduces the caffeine content of coffee to the range of 0.03% to 1.2% caffeine. The extracted caffeine is used in various pharmaceutical products, such as APC tablets.

Among coffee lovers, there is some controversy about the best method to remove the caffeine from coffee beans. **Direct contact** decaffeination uses an organic solvent (usually methylene chloride) to remove the caffeine from the beans. When the beans are subsequently roasted at 200°C, virtually all traces of the solvent are removed, because methylene chloride boils at 40°C. The advantage of direct contact decaffeination is that the method removes only the caffeine (and some waxes) but leaves the substances responsible for the flavor of the coffee intact in the bean. A disadvantage of this method is that all organic solvents are toxic to some extent.

Water process decaffeination is favored among many drinkers of decaffeinated coffee because it does not use organic solvents. In this method, hot water and steam are used to remove caffeine and other soluble substances from the coffee. The resulting solution is then passed through activated charcoal filters to remove the caffeine. Although this method does not use organic solvents, the disadvantage is that water is not a very selective de-caffeinating agent. Many of the flavor oils in the coffee are removed at the same time, resulting in a coffee with a somewhat bland flavor.

A third method, the **carbon dioxide decaffeination process,** is being used with increasing frequency. The raw coffee beans are moistened with steam and water, and they are then placed into an extractor where they are treated with carbon dioxide gas under very high temperature and pressure. Under these conditions, the carbon dioxide gas is in a **supercritical** state, which means that it takes on the characteristics of both a liquid and a gas. The supercritical carbon dioxide acts as a selective solvent for caffeine, thus extracting it from the beans.

Caffeine has always been a controversial compound. Medically, its actions are suspect. It definitely has strong effects on the heart and blood vessels, causing an increase in blood pressure. It stimulates the central nervous system, making a person more alert but also more jittery. Many people consider caffeine to be a dangerous and addictive drug, and some religions forbid the use of beverages containing caffeine for this very reason.

Another problem, not related to caffeine but rather to the beverage tea, is that in some cases persons who consume high quantities of tea may show symptoms of Vitamin B_1 (thiamine) deficiency. It is suggested that the tannins in the tea may complex with the thiamine, rendering it unavailable for use. An alternative suggestion is that caffeine may reduce the levels of the enzyme transketolase, which depends on the presence of thiamine for its activity. Lowered levels of transketolase would produce the same symptoms as lowered levels of thiamine.

REFERENCES

Emboden, W. "The Stimulants." *Narcotic Plants*, rev. ed. New York: Macmillan, 1979.

Ray, O. S. "Caffeine." *Drugs, Society and Human Behavior*, 7th ed. St. Louis: C. V. Mosby, 1996.

Ritchie, J. M. "Central Nervous System Stimulants. II: The Xanthines." In L. S. Goodman and A. Gilman, eds., *The Pharmacological Basis of Therapeutics*, 8th ed. New York: Macmillan, 1990.

Taylor, N. *Plant Drugs That Changed the World.* New York: Dodd, Mead, 1965. Pp. 54–56.

Taylor, N. "Three Habit-Forming Nondangerous Beverages." In *Narcotics— Nature's Dangerous Gifts.* New York: Dell, 1970. (Paperbound revision of *Flight from Reality*.)

ISOLATION OF CAFFEINE FROM TEA OR COFFEE

Caffeine can be isolated from tea leaves or cofee beans. The chief problem with the isolation is that caffeine does not exist alone in tea leaves or coffee beans, but is accompanied by other natural substances from which it must be separated. The main component of tea leaves is cellulose, which is the principal structural material of all plant cells. Cellulose is a polymer of glucose. Because cellulose is virtually insoluble in water, it presents no problems in the isolation procedure. Caffeine, on the other hand, is water soluble and is one of the main substances extracted into the solution called tea. Caffeine constitutes as much as 5% by weight of the leaf material in tea plants.

Tannins also dissolve in the hot water used to extract tea leaves. The term **tannin** does not refer to a single homogeneous compound or even to substances that have similar chemical structure. It refers to a class of compounds that have certain properties in common. Tannins are phenolic compounds having molecular weights between 500 and 3000. They are widely used to tan leather. They precipitate alkaloids and proteins from aqueous solutions. Tannins are usually divided into two classes: those that can be **hydrolyzed** (react with water) and those that cannot. Tannins of the first type that are found in tea generally yield glucose and gallic acid when they are hydrolyzed. These tannins are esters of gallic acid and glucose. They represent structures in which some of the hydroxyl groups in glucose have been esterified by digalloyl groups. The nonhydrolyzable tannins found in tea are condensation polymers of catechin. These polymers are not uniform in structure; catechin molecules are usually linked at ring positions 4 and 8.

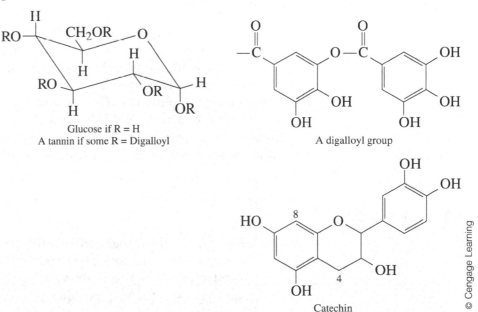

Glucose if R = H
A tannin if some R = Digalloyl

A digalloyl group

Catechin

When tannins are extracted into hot water, some of these compounds are partially hydrolyzed to form free gallic acid. The tannins, because of their phenolic groups, and gallic acid, because of its carboxyl groups, are both acidic. If sodium carbonate, a base, is added to tea water, these acids are converted to their sodium salts that are highly soluble in water.

Although caffeine is soluble in water, it is much more soluble in the organic solvent methylene chloride. Caffeine can be extracted from the basic tea solution with methylene chloride, but the sodium salts of gallic acid and the tannins remain in the aqueous layer.

The brown color of a tea solution is due to flavonoid pigments and chlorophylls and to their respective oxidation products. Although chlorophylls are soluble in methylene chloride, most other substances in tea are not. Thus, the methylene chloride extraction of the basic tea solution removes nearly pure caffeine. The methylene chloride is easily removed by evaporation to leave the crude caffeine. The caffeine is then purified by sublimation at reduced pressure to prevent decomposition.

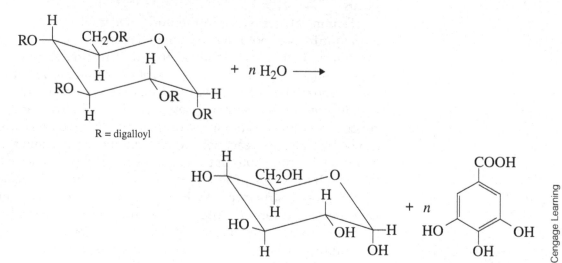

Methylene chloride solvent is toxic and a suspected carcinogen, but it remains as one of the best solvents for extracting caffeine from aqueous tea and coffee solutions. Other solvents simply do not do as good a job of extracting caffeine. Besides being toxic, chlorinated solvents are also environmental pollutants. This solvent must be disposed of correctly to avoid environmental problems. Ethyl acetate is "more Green" than methylene chloride, but unfortunately it does not extract caffeine from aqueous solutions nearly as efficiently as methylene chloride.

PROCEDURE

1. Take 20 g of pre-ground coffee in the espresso maker and use 250 mL of water to make the coffee (your TA will help you in this step). Collect the coffee in a beaker containing 6.0 g of $CaCO_3$.

2. Gently heat this mixture to about 70°C on a hot plate for 10 minutes.

3. Cool and then filter using a fritted funnel with Celite (filter aid). If foaming occurs in the filter flask, remove the vacuum immediately until the foaming subsides.

4. Transfer the filtrate evenly into two separatory funnels and extract with 4 × 20 mL of CH_2Cl_2. Gently roll the separatory funnel – DO NOT SHAKE! Collect and pool the organic layers after the extractions.

5. Dry the combined organic layer with anhydrous $MgSO_4$; filter and discard the insoluble solids; transfer the filtrate to a 250 mL round bottom flask.

6. Evaporate the solution using a rotary evaporator. This will give you the crude caffeine.

7. Recrystallize the crude product from acetone-petroleum ether. In order to do this, dissolve the crude compound in a small volume of hot acetone and add enough petroleum ether to make the solution cloudy. Cool the solution in an ice bath.

8. Filter the crystals using a Hirsch funnel, weigh them and calculate the percent of caffeine isolated based on the weight of ground coffee.

9. Determine the melting point of the recrystallized caffeine.

QUESTIONS

1. Why was calcium carbonate added to the mixture?

2. Give two explanations for an experimental caffeine melting point that is lower than the literature value.

Deducing a Reaction Mechanism for the Isomerization of Maleic Acid to Fumaric Acid

Prepared by J.S. Meek

In 1785, the Swedish chemist Karl Scheele first isolated malic acid from green apples. Malic acid is also found in other fruits as well. Malic acid has the structure shown below. Two isomeric acids, maleic and fumaric acid, can be derived from the dehydration of malic acid. Both acids have the same molecular formula, but different melting points. Maleic and Fumaric acids are *cis* and *trans* stereoisomers. Maleic acid was found to easily lose water to form a cyclic anhydride, and it was therefore determined to be the *cis* isomer. Fumaric acid cannot form a cyclic anhydride by heating. In 1884, Kekulé and Strecker showed that when maleic acid was heated with diluted hydrochloric acid, it rapidly converted to fumaric acid. There are at least eight possible mechanisms for this isomerization reaction. In this experiment, you will carry out a variety of tests to determine which mechanism is potentially operative.

Meek, J.S., "The Determination of a Mechanism of Isomerization of Maleic Acid to Fumaric Acid." Adapted with permission from The Journal of Chemical Education, Vol. 52, No. 1, 1975, pp. 541–543. Copyright © 2009, 1975, Division of Chemical Education, Inc.

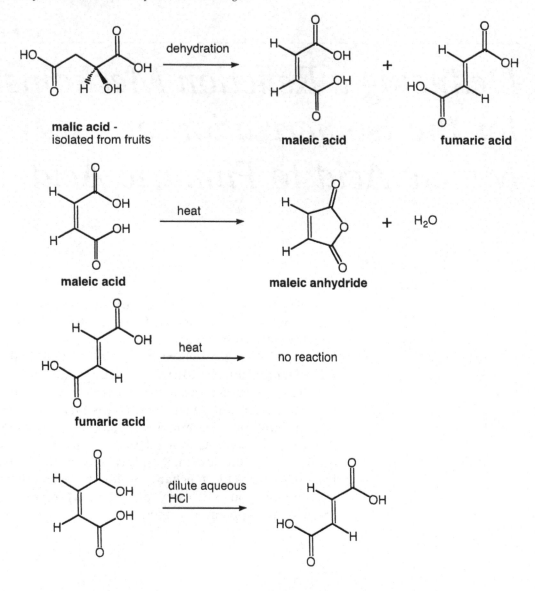

**malic acid -
isolated from fruits**

maleic acid

fumaric acid

maleic acid

maleic anhydride

fumaric acid

POSSIBLE MECHANISMS FOR THE ISOMERIZATION

1. Maleic acid is activated by visible light, and then rearranges to form fumaric acid. In this mechanism, the pi-bond is momentarily broken, allowing for the free rotation to give the more stable *trans* isomer. The double bond then reforms.

2. The rearrangement of maleic acid to fumaric acid is accomplished by the thermal excitation of the molecule. In this mechanism, the pi-bond is broken by the application of heat. As described above, this would allow rotation to occur and form the more stable *trans* isomer.

3. A nudeophilic addition of a chloride ion to maleic acid again permits free rotation, followed by release of the Cl⁻ ion to product fumaric acid:

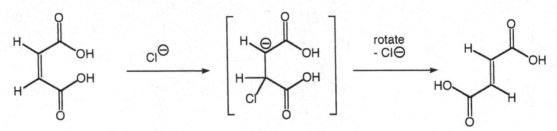

4. An electrophilic addition of a proton to maleic acid, followed by rotation and then deprotonation.

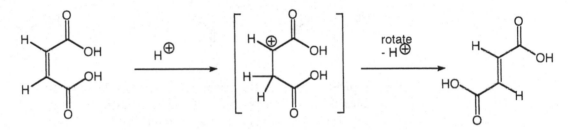

5. Water adds to maleic acid (under acid catalysis) to form malic acid. Malic acid then rotates to a new conformation and elimates water to form fumaric acid.

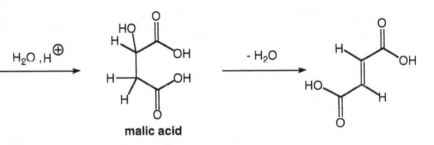

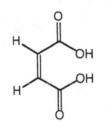

malic acid

6. The addition of a proton to maleic acid leads to the formation of a lactone (cyclic ester), which undergoes a ring opening reaction to yield malic acid. Malic acid is then dehydrated to give fumaric acid.

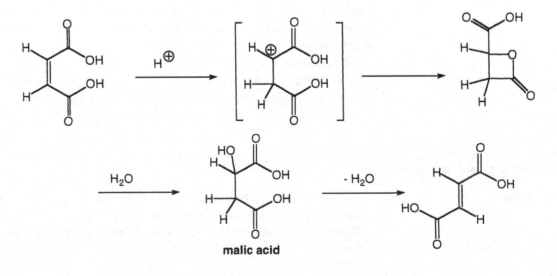

malic acid

7. A proton adds to the carbonyl oxygen to give an intermediate with a number of resonance structures. One of these resonance structures can freely rotate and deprotonation will give fumaric acid.

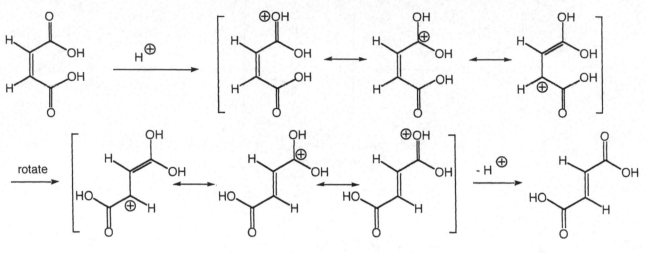

8. A proton adds to the carbonyl oxygen, followed by an addition of a chloride ion. The product of this 1,4 addition then undergoes a free rotation, and hydrochloric acid is eliminated to produce fumaric acid.

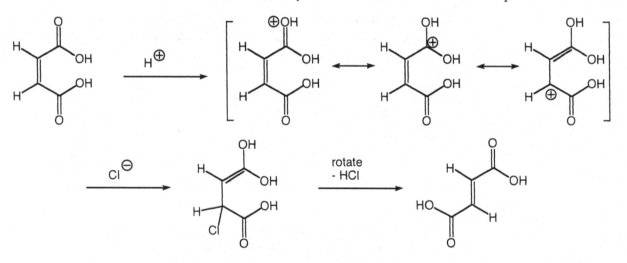

In this experiment you will attempt to carry out the isomerization reaction under six different reaction conditions. Each of the specified conditions should allow you to eliminate one or more of the possible mechanisms.

In chemistry, it is usually easier to disprove a reaction mechanism than to prove one. However, if you can safely eliminate seven of the eight mechanisms given above, you can be reasonably certain that remaining mechanism is close to the true state of affairs.

THE EXPERIMENT

Procedure

Prepare a water bath at about 80°C with a large beaker of water on a hot plate. Label six large test tubes with the letters A–F. Add the appropriate solids to each test tube first. Then add the appropriate solvent to each test tube.

Table 1 *Test tube contents*

Test Tube	Solids	Solvents
A	1.0 g maleic acid	3.0 mL 6M HCl
B	1.0 g maleic acid	3.0 mL 3M H_2SO_4
C	1.0 g maleic acid 0.5 g ammonium chloride	3.0 mL distilled water
D	1.0 g maleic acid 0.5 g ammonium chloride	3.0 mL 6M HCl
E	1.0 g malic acid	3.0 mL 6M HCl
F	1.0 g maleic acid	1.5 mL distilled water 2.0 mL conc. HBr

Place all the marked test tubes in the hot-water bath and stir the contents of each test tube vigorously until all the solids dissolve.

NOTE: You must use a separate stirring rod in each test tube to avoid cross contamination. Allow the samples to remain in the water bath for 40 minutes. Observe and record which samples form precipitates, and the relative speed of the reaction (after how many minutes did precipitates begin forming).

Do not cool the test tubes, but collect each precipitate from the hot reaction mixture by vacuum filtration using a Hirsch funnel. Wash each precipitate in the filter paper with 10 mL of warm water, and allow each precipitate to dry. To aid drying, you may place the precipitate on a new dry filter paper, and use a paper towel to pat it dry.

Record the melting point for each solid obtained. Using the table of solubilities and melting points on the next page, determine the identity of each solid.

Table 2 *Solubility and melting point data*

Compound	mp (°C)	Relative Solubility in warm water
l-malic acid	99–100	very soluble
dl-malic acid	128–129	very soluble
maleic acid	139–140	very soluble
fumaric acid	300–302	fairly insoluble

ANALYSIS OF MECHANISM

1. Is visible light solely responsible for the isomerization of maleic acid to fumaric acid? Explain.

2. If the isomerization of maleic acid to fumaric acid is a thermal effect, which test tubes should contain fumaric acid?

3. For mechanism 3 to be correct, which test tubes should contain fumaric acid?

4. For mechanism 4 to be correct, which test tubes should contain fumaric acid?

5. For mechanism 5 to be correct, which test tubes must contain fumaric acid?

6. Which test might rule out mechanism 6 as a possibility?

7. For mechanism 7 to be correct, which test tubes must contain fumaric acid?

8. For mechanism 8 to be correct, which test tubes must contain fumaric acid?

ADDITIONAL QUESTIONS

1. Does sulfuric acid, which ionizes to give a negatively charged sulfate ion, induce the isomerization of maleic acid to fumaric acid? Explain.

2. Based upon your observations, would you expect fumaric acid to form in a test tube containing 1 g of maleic acid, 0.5 g NH_4Cl, and 3 mL of $3M$ H_2SO_4, after it was heated? Explain.

Cyclohexene

Prepared by Donald L. Pavia, Gary M. Lampman
and George S. Kriz, Western Washington University

INTRODUCTION

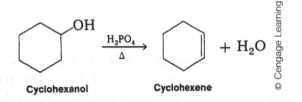

Cyclohexanol   Cyclohexene

Alcohol dehydration is an acid-catalyzed reaction performed by strong, concentrated mineral acids, such as sulfuric and phosphoric acids. The acids protonate the alcoholic hydroxyl group, permitting it to dissociate as water. Loss of a proton from the intermediate (elimination) brings about an alkene. Since sulfuric acid often causes extensive charring in this reaction, phosphoric acid, which is comparatively free of this problem, will be used.

The equilibrium that attends this reaction will be shifted in favor of the product, cyclohexene, by distilling it from the reaction mixture as it is formed. The cyclohexene will co-distill with the water that is also formed. By continuously removing the products, one can obtain a high yield of cyclohexene. Since the starting material, cyclohexanol, is also rather low-boiling, the distillation must be done carefully, not allowing the temperature to rise much above 100°C.

Unavoidably, a small amount of phosphoric acid co-distills with the products. It is removed by washing the distillate mixture with aqueous sodium carbonate. To remove the water that co-distills with cyclohexene, and any traces of water introduced in the base extraction, the product will be dried over anhydrous sodium sulfate.

Compounds containing double bonds react with a bromine solution (red) to decolorize it. Similarly, they react with a solution of potassium permanganate (purple) to discharge its color and produce a brown

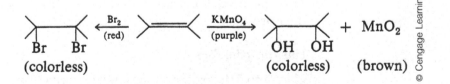

CENGAGE Learning

precipitate (MnO_2). These reactions are often used as qualitative tests to determine the presence of a double bond in an organic molecule. Both tests will be performed on the cyclohexene formed in this experiment.

SPECIAL INSTRUCTIONS

Phosphoric acid is very corrosive. Do not allow any acid to touch your skin.

PROCEDURE

Apparatus Assembly

Place 10 mL of cyclohexanol and 2.5 mL of 85% phosphoric acid in a 50-mL round-bottom flask. Mix the liquids thoroughly using a glass stirring rod and add a boiling stone. Assemble a distillation apparatus, using a 25-mL flask as a receiver. Immerse the receiving flask in an ice-water bath to minimize the possibility that cyclohexene vapor will escape into the laboratory.

Dehydration

Start circulating the cooling water in the condenser and heat the mixture until the product begins to distill and collect in the receiver. The heating should be regulated so that the temperature of the distilling vapor does not exceed 100°C. Too rapid distillation leads to incomplete reaction and isolation of the starting material, cyclohexanol. Continue the distillation until no more liquid is collected. The distillate contains cyclohexene, water, and possibly some H_3PO_4.

Isolation and Drying the Product

Saturate the distillate with solid sodium chloride. Add the salt, little by little, and shake the flask gently. When no more salt will dissolve, add enough saturated aqueous sodium carbonate solution to make the distilled solution basic to litmus. Pour the mixture into a separatory funnel and separate the two layers. Drain the aqueous layer through the stopcock and then pour the upper layer (cyclohexene) through the neck of the separatory funnel into a 50 mL Erlenmeyer flask. Add anhydrous sodium sulfate to the flask and swirl occasionally until the solution appears dry. During this time, perform the unsaturation tests on the neutralized crude (partially dry) product.

Unsaturation Tests

Place 4 to 5 drops of cyclohexanol in each of two small test tubes. In each of another two small test tubes, place 4 to 5 drops of the cyclohexene you prepared. Don't confuse the test tubes. Take one test tube from each group and add to the contents of each a solution of bromine in carbon tetrachloride, drop by drop, until the red color is no longer discharged. Record the result in each case. Test the remaining two test tubes in a similar fashion with a solution of potassium permanganate. Since aqueous potassium permanganate is not miscible with organic compounds, you will have to add about 0.3 mL of 1,2-dimethoxyethane to each test tube before making the test. Record your results and explain them.

Distillation

Reassemble a distillation apparatus as before, using a *pre weighed* 25-mL receiving flask. Again, cool the receiver in an ice-water bath. Decant the dry cyclohexene solution into the distilling flask and add a boiling stone. Distill the cyclohexene and collect the material that boils over the range of 80 to 85°C. Reweigh the receiving flask to determine how much cyclohexene you prepared and calculate the yield. Reflect on the purity of your sample by analyzing the boiling point of the distillate.

QUESTIONS

1. Draw a mechanism for the dehydration of cyclohexanol catalyzed by phosphoric acid.

2. What alkene would be produced on dehydration of each of the following alcohols?

   a. 1-Methylcyclohexanol

   b. 2-Methylcyclohexanol

   c. 4-Methylcyclohexanol

   d. 2,2-Dimethylcyclohexanol

   e. 1,2-Cyclohexanediol

3. In the work-up procedure for cyclohexene, why is salt added before the layers are neutralized and separated?

4. What is the purpose of adding the sodium carbonate solution? Give an equation.

High-Performance Liquid Chromatography (HPLC) Analysis of Pharmaceuticals and Derivatives

Prepared by Dr. Gary Stolzenberg and the Sibi Group,
North Dakota State University

INTRODUCTION

In this exercise you will use column chromatography to separate and quantify some of the over-the-counter drugs and/or derivatives of these drugs analyzed earlier by thin-layer chromatography (TLC). Recall that TLC can resolve only 4–8 components per sample, depending on the individual Rf values. In your TLC work, samples were applied to a polar stationary phase (silica gel = finely-divided polymeric SiO_2) on a flexible support sheet. They were then mobilized (desorbed and caused to migrate) with a relatively non-polar solvent, one selected or blended so that the sample's most mobile (least polar) component remained below the solvent front.

As with gas chromatography (GC), liquid chromatography, especially HPLC, can separate many components (often greater than 35 components). HPLC results often are reported as retention times, similar to GC. You will apply simple isocratic (constant solvent composition) HPLC to solutions of some non-volatile solid drugs or derivatives which are not analyzable by conventional GC techniques.

The HPLC column used with these drugs is *not* filled with a conventional polar stationary phase like silica gel. Instead it uses a reversed-phase packing of finely-divided silica that has been derivatized with covalently-bonded alkyl groups making the stationary phase non-polar. Thus, it retains organic compounds largely in proportion to hydrocarbon content, and retention is decreased by polar substituents such as hydroxyls, carboxyls, carbonyls, amines, etc. Reversed-phase (RP) columns are offered by many firms; most are secretive about production methods. The lipophilic substituents often are octadecylsilyl (or, ODS) groups; thus the term "C_{18}-RP-HPLC" refers to alkyl chains 18-carbons long attached to the silica.

A typical HPLC system has some pre-column components: the solvent pump and a sample injector. The sample mixture enters a column for separation through the injector and the mobile phase is pumped through the system. The usual post-column HPLC component is some type of detector, often one measuring light absorption in the near-ultraviolet (typically at 254 or 280 nm). Samples with aromatic rings or carbonyl groups strongly absorb these wavelengths; thus, solvents like benzene, toluene or acetone cannot be used. In C18-RP-HPLC, the solvent often is a mixture of water (highly purified, possibly with some buffer or salt) and methanol (or the more costly acetonitrile). These are transparent at the wavelengths of interest and do not interfere with detection of the samples.

HPLC techniques are applied extensively and routinely in biological and chemical analyses. Because clinical laboratories and medical researchers often use water-based samples (blood serum, culture broth, urine), RP-HPLC procedures may be the method of choice. Such samples often undergo a preliminary cleanup and pre-concentration by a related RP technique, solid-phase extraction (SPE): the aqueous sample is passed through a filter or "bed" with a C_{18} or similar RP coating which strongly retains many organics; this bed is washed with water to remove peptides, buffer salts, sugars, etc. Then the biochemical or pharmacological components of interest are eluted rapidly (without any separation) with a small volume of methanol or other solvent.

PHARMACEUTICAL ANALYSIS BY HPLC

All chromatographic techniques depend on the *separation* of two or more materials as they *distribute/partition* between two *phases*: one is *stationary* (a solid or an immobilized liquid) while the other is *mobile* (a liquid or gas).

The results from these procedures are collected/presented as a "chromatogram": an elution/mobility report of the abundance/concentration/intensity/response (for different materials) vs. time.

The basic analytical concepts are that light absorption depends on the specific properties of the sample, the particular wavelength used for the analysis, analyte concentration, and the thickness of the solution layer (path length). This is expressed in the Bouguer-Beer (or Beer-Lambert) law as

$$A = \log(l_0/l) = \varepsilon bc$$

where "A" is the absorption, "l_0/l" is the ratio of the light intensities before and after passing through the analyte, "ε" is the extinction coefficient, "b" is the path length, and "c" is the analyte's concentration.

These HPLC units provide a tracing (chromatogram) of the peak intensity vs. retention time (RT) as each component reaches the detector, attains its maximum concentration, and is washed away. The chromatogram's report also lists each peak as an individual area and as an area % of the total area of all the peaks (100%, including other analytes plus impurities). Thus, when a known amount of any material is injected into the HPLC system, the peak area at the RT of that unique material is used to calculate a response factor (area unit/microgram, etc) for that particular analyte. If different amounts are injected, one can construct a calibration curve by plotting response (area units on the *y*-axis) vs. sample amount (micrograms, mg/mL, etc. on the *x*-axis). This takes the form of a line where each compound has its own calibration curve.

PROCEDURE

Each team is to prepare a reference solution with carefully-weighed amounts (nearest 0.0001 gram = 0.1 mg) of the 3 compounds listed below. A TA will assist at the analytical balances. High-purity (HPLC-grade) solvents (85:15 water: acetonitrile) will be used for this work.

Component	RT (mins)
4-Acetamidophenol = Acetaminophen	~4
Acetylsalicylic acid = Aspirin	~6
Caffeine = 1,3,7-Trimethylxanthine	~7

Reference Solution

Weigh out 3–6 mg (0.003–0.006 g) of each component and combine into a solvent-rinsed 100-ml volumetric flask (or 2–4 mg into a 50-ml flask). Dissolve them in the pre-mixed chromatographic solvent (possibly by warming, then cooling) and fill to the mark.

A TA will inject a portion (usually 20 microliters = 0.020 mL) onto the RP-C_{18} column. You will receive a copy of the data (tracing of UV absorption vs. time; list of retention time and integrated area for any peak). You will also be provided with data from additional standard solutions. Each team is to plot the 3 calibration curves or calculate the "response factors" (254-nm peak area/microgram) from these data.

Each team's "unknown" solution will contain 1–3 components (of those listed above) at unspecified concentrations. After this unknown is analyzed by C_{18}-RP-HPLC, use the recorder's chart plus your calibration line(s) to identify the components present and their respective concentrations (in mg/mL).

Attention to detail, careful work, and decontamination are critical! With less than 1 microgram of any standard, the trace may be greater than two times off-scale. A peak height of 1/3 the chart's width may result from less than 0.01 microgram of contamination.

Suggestions for the Laboratory Report

Introduction. Include team's names!

Experimental. Include structures of the compounds. The isocratic solvent, 15% acetonitrile and 0.40% triethyl-ammonium acetate (as triethylamine + acetic acid) by volume in water, is pumped at 1.60 mL/min through the 4.6(i.d.) × 250 (length)-mm C_{18}-RP (on fine-grained silica) column.

Data. Include a copy of the recorder's charts in at least one team member's report. Show all calculations; Identify and quantify (in mg/mL) your sample's components.

Discussion/Question(s). Submit your calibration curves as a computer-generated plot. Indicate on any plots those points that are your group's data!

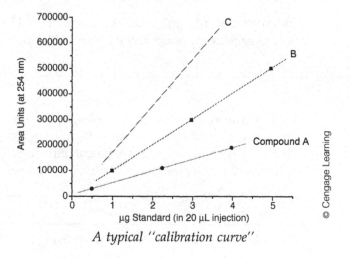

A typical "calibration curve"

REFERENCES

1. Day Jr., R.A. & Underwood, A.L., 1986, Quantitative Analysis, 5th ed., Prentice-Hall, pp. 428–433.
2. Fereguson, Glenda J. Chem. Educ. 1998, 75, 467–469.

QUESTIONS

1. What is the difference between normal-phase HPLC and reversed-phase HPLC?

2. Predict the order of elution for a mixture of biphenyl, benzoic acid, and benzyl alcohol using reversed-phase HPLC.

Preparation of Polyesters

Prepared by Donald L. Pavia, Gary M. Lampman and George S. Kriz, Western Washington University, and Richard Engel, Edmonds Community College; and Karla Radke, North Dakota State University

INTRODUCTION

Polymers are widespread in the world around us. Everyday encounters with polymers include the plastic bags in which we carry our groceries, the rubber on the soles of our shoes, the paints and coatings on our vehicles, the cellulose which constitutes this piece of paper, the proteins which make up our hair and skin, and the DNA (deoxyribonucleic acid) which serves as blueprints for all living organisms. The aforementioned polymers are just a few examples selected from a vast list of polymers we encounter daily.

Polymers are large chain-like molecules which are made up of many (>10) repeating units. Polymer is a term derived from the Greek words poly and meros which translate literally to "many parts." Each of these many parts (repeat units) are individually referred to as **monomers** ("one part"). **Oligomers** ("few parts") are molecules made up of 2–10 monomers. Classes of polymers are named according to the functional group in the monomer along with the prefix poly-. For example, polymers made from carbonates are called polycarbonates (Fig. 1).

Since it would be nearly impossible to write the complete structure of many polymers, polymers are instead depicted by writing the monomer unit inside brackets. The number of repeat units is signified by a subscript to the right of the brackets. For example, the structure in Fig. 1. is a polycarbonate composed of 23 repeat units. When the number of repeat units is unknown, an "n" is subscripted to the right of the brackets to indicate that the unit is repeated n times.

Figure 1
A polycarbonate

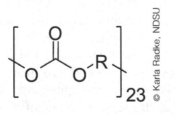

© Karla Radke, NDSU

Polymers can be classified according to how they are synthesized, step-growth or chain-growth. A **step-growth polymer** results from random unions of monomer units and typically forms a small molecule as a byproduct which is referred to as condensation. A **chain-growth polymer**

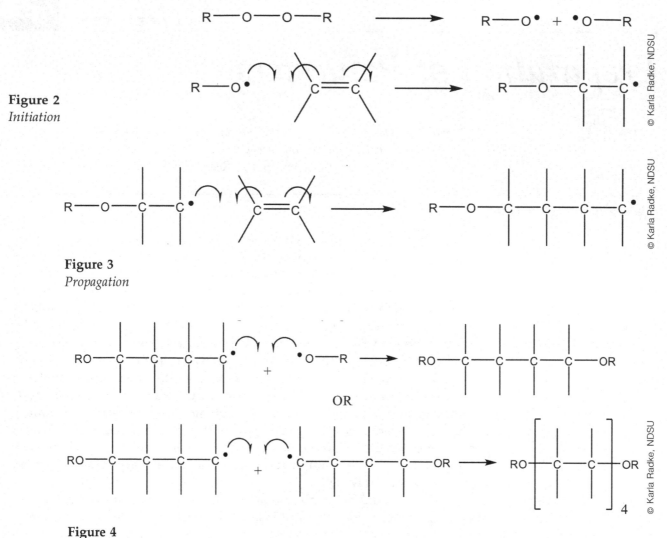

Figure 2
Initiation

Figure 3
Propagation

Figure 4
Termination

results from a three-step process (initiation, propagation, and termination) where monomer units are added to the end of a growing chain. Most chain-growth polymerizations are referred to as addition processes because the polymer contains the same atoms as were present in the monomer. Fig. 2, 3, and 4 illustrate the free-radical chain-growth process using a peroxide and a vinyl monomer (ethylene).

Polymers can also be described as **linear** or **crosslinked** (among other types). A linear polymer is a straight-chain molecule formed from monomers linked together through reaction of two sites of the monomer. A crosslinked polymer is formed from reaction of more than two sites of the monomer unit. Even though a linear polymer and a crosslinked polymer may have similar monomer units, the manner in which the units are joined can result in very different bulk properties of the polymers. In this experiment, you will prepare and compare physical properties of one linear polyester (Figure 5) and one crosslinked, step-growth polyester (Figure 6).

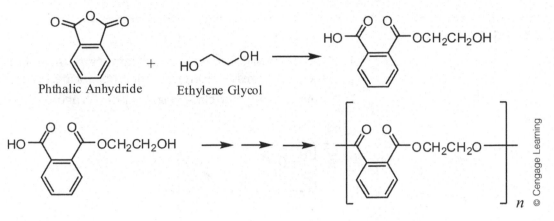

Figure 5
Preparation of a linear polyester

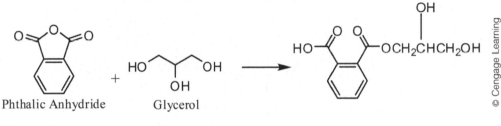

Figure 6
Preparation of a monomer which can form a crosslinked polyester

PROCEDURE

Label two tests tubes A and B. Add 1 g of phthalic anhydride, 0.05 g sodium acetate, and a boiling stone to tube A. Repeat with tube B. To tube A, add 8 drops of ethylene glycol. To tube B, add 8 drops of glycerol. Heat both tubes in a sand bath (about 5 cm of sand in a beaker) while monitoring the temperature of the sand. The temperature should be held between 200 and 250 °C. Heat the tubes for 5 minutes after they start to boil. Carefully pour the contents of the tubes onto 2 watch glasses labeled A and B. Compare the viscosity of the two solutions while they are being poured. Allow the samples to cool before making further physical observations.

QUESTIONS

1. Draw a crosslinked oligomer (composed of at least 4 repeat units) which could result from the monomer formed in test tube B.

2. Name the polymer class based on the structure given.

a.

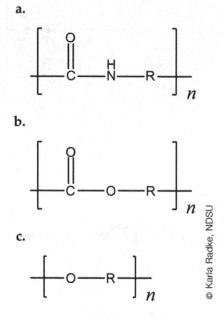

b.

c.

Competitive Nucleophiles

Prepared by Donald L. Pavia, Gary M. Lampman and George S. Kriz, Western Washington University, and Richard Engel, Edmonds Community College

INTRODUCTION

The purpose of this experiment is to compare the relative nucleophilicities of chloride ions and bromide ions toward *n*-butyl alcohol and toward *t*-pentyl alcohol. The two nucleophiles will be present at the same time in each reaction, in equimolar concentrations, and they will be competing with each other for the substrate.

In general, alcohols do not react readily in simple nucleophilic displacement reactions. If they are attacked by nucleophiles directly, the hydroxide ion, a strong base, must be displaced. Such a displacement is not energetically favorable and it cannot occur to any reasonable extent.

$$X^- + ROH \longrightarrow\!\!\!/\!\!\!\longrightarrow R\!-\!X + OH^-$$

To avoid this problem, one must carry out nucleophilic displacement reactions with alcohols as substrates in acidic media. In a rapid initial step, the alcohol is protonated; then water, a very stable molecule, is displaced. This displacement is energetically very favorable and the reaction proceeds in high yield.

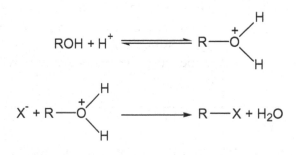

Once the alcohol is protonated, the substrate reacts by either the S_N1 or the S_N2 mechanism, depending on the structure of the alkyl group of the alcohol. For a brief review of these mechanisms, you should consult the nucleophilic substitution sections in your textbook.

You will analyze the products of the two reactions studied in this experiment by refractometry to determine the relative amounts of alkyl chloride and alkyl bromide formed in each reaction. That is, using equimolar concentrations of chloride ions and bromide ions reacting against both n-butyl alcohol (1-butanol) and t-pentyl alcohol (2-methyl-2-butanol), you will try to determine which ion is the better nucleophile and for which of the two substrates (reactions) this difference is important. The ammonium halides (NH_4Cl and NH_4Br) are used as sources of halide ions in this experiment since they are more soluble at the concentrations required than are the corresponding sodium or potassium salts.

SPECIAL INSTRUCTIONS

Before beginning this experiment, review the appropriate chapters in your lecture textbook. Sulfuric acid is very corrosive, be careful when handling it.

Procedures

Before preparing the nucleophile mixture and carrying out the reaction, assemble an apparatus for reflux in a fume hood using a 100-mL round-bottomed flask and a condenser. The gas trap is not needed. A heating mantle is used as a heating source. In addition, on a separate ring stand, a 125-mL separatory funnel should be ready and resting in a ring.

The Solvent-Nucleophile Medium

Place 44 mL of pre-diluted (~7.7 mol/L) sulfuric acid in a 125-mL Erlenmeyer flask. Carefully weigh 4.75 g of ammonium chloride and 8.75 g of ammonium bromide into a 125-mL beaker. Crush any lumps of these reagents to powder, and then, using a powder funnel, transfer these halides to a 250-mL Erlenmeyer flask. Using caution, add the sulfuric acid mixture to the ammonium salts a little at a time. Swirl the mixture vigorously to induce the salts to dissolve. It will probably be necessary to heat the mixture on a hot plate to achieve total solution. If necessary, you may add as much as 2.5 mL of water at this stage.

When solution has been achieved, allow the liquid to cool slightly and then pour 17 mL of it into the separatory funnel and the reminder into the reflux apparatus. A small portion of the salts in the separatory funnel or the boiling flask or both may precipitate as the solution cools. Do not worry about these at this point; they will redissolve during the reaction.

PROCEDURE A

Competitive Nucleophiles with 1-Butanol

Add 2.5 mL of 1-butanol to the solvent-nucleophile mixture contained in the reflux apparatus and add a boiling stone. Start circulating the cooling water. Adjust the heat from the heating mantle so that this mixture maintains a gentle boiling action. Be very careful to adjust the reflux ring so that it remains in the lower fourth of the condenser. Violent boiling will cause loss of product. Continue heating the mixture for 75 minutes. During this heating period, go on to Procedure B and finish it before returning to this prodedure.

When the period of reflux has been completed, discontinue heating, remove the heating mantle, and allow the reaction mixture to cool. Be careful not to shake the hot solution as you remove the heating mantle, or a violent boiling and bubbling action will result; this could allow material to be lost out the top of the condenser. Prepare a bath of ice and water, and cool the reaction mixture by immersing the boiling flask in the bath. After a few minutes, it will be possible to swirl the reaction mixture with safety, thereby increasing the efficiency of cooling. Do not remove the condenser until the reaction mixture is cool.

Transfer the cooled solution to a 125-mL separatory funnel, taking care to leave behind any solids that may have precipitated. Allow the phases to separate and drain the lower layer. If the reaction was not yet complete, some 1-butanol may remain, which in some case may form a second organic layer; that is, there will be three layers. Treat both of these organic layers as if they were one, and add 5 mL of water to them. Shake this mixture in the separatory funnel, allow the layers to separate, and once again drain the lower layer. Extract this organic layer with 5 mL of saturated sodium bicarbonate solution, separate the layers, and drain the organic layer into a 25-mL Erlenmeyer flask before drying with anhydrous sodium sulfate. When the solution is clear, decant the halide solution into a clean, dry, ground-glass stoppered flask (25-mL), taking care not to transfer any solid. This sample can now be analyzed by refractometry.

PROCEDURE B

Competitive Nucleophiles with 2-Methyl-2-Butanol

Carefully measure 2.5 mL of 2-methyl-2-butanol (*t*-pentyl alcohol) using a graduated cylinder, and add it to the separatory funnel containing the other portion of the solvent-nucleophile medium, which should be cooled to room temperature by this time. Replace the stopper, carefully swirl the funnel a couple of times, and then invert it to release the mixing pressure. Repeat this until the pressure are substantially equalized; then invert the funnel and shake it vigorously, with occasional venting, for 2 minutes. Any solids that were originally present in the funnel should be dissolved during this period. After shaking, place the funnel in a ring and allow the layer of alkyl halides to separate. A fairly distinct layer should have formed by this time. Slowly drain the lower layer into a beaker. After waiting 10–15 seconds, drain another small portion of the material in the funnel, including a small amount of the organic layer, so as to be certain that it is not contaminated by any water. Then drain the remainder of the alkyl halide layer into a small beaker or flask containing about 0.5 g of solid sodium bicarbonate. As soon as the bubbling stops and clear liquid is obtained, decant it into a clean, dry, ground-glass, stoppered flask (25-mL), taking care not to transfer any solid. This sample can now be analyzed by refractometry.

ANALYSIS PROCEDURE

Refractive Index

Measure the refractive index of the product mixture. To determine the composition of the mixture, assume a linear relation between the refractive index and the molar composition of the mixture. The temperature and refractive indices for the four standards will be recorded on the board.

Using the equations given below, calculate and record the percentages of alkyl chloride (Eqn 1) and alkyl bromide (Eqn 2) in the reaction mixture.

$$\%\text{Cl} = \frac{\text{RI(Br)} - \text{RI(prod)}}{\text{RI(Br)} - \text{RI(Cl)}} * 100\% \qquad \text{(Eq. 1)}$$

$$\%\text{Br} = 100\% - \%\text{Cl} \qquad \text{(Eq. 2)}$$

QUESTIONS

1. Draw complete mechanisms that explain the resultant product distributions observed for the reactions of 1-butanol and 2-methyl-2-butanol under the reaction conditions of this experiment.

2. Which is the better nucleophile, chloride ion or bromide ion? Try to explain this in the terms of the nature of the chloride ion and the bromide ion.

N-Acetylanthranilic Acid:
A Highly Triboluminescent Material

Prepared by the Department of Chemistry and Molecular Biology,
North Dakota State University

INTRODUCTION

Triboluminescence, the emission of light when a crystal is broken, has been known for some time but remains an obscure phenomenon even though many inorganic and organic materials are reported to exhibit this property.[1] The effect has been explained by excitation of the molecule by an electric discharge between the surfaces of the fractured crystal and subsequent fluorescence.

In the course of the laboratory preparation of 2-methylbenzisoxazinone,[2,3] it is noted that its hydrolysis product, N-acetylanthranilic acid, is highly triboluminescent and this serves to make the experiment more interesting than the synthesis itself.

In the experiment, anthranilic acid is converted to 2-methylbenzisoxazinone by the action of acetic anhydride. This compound may be isolated or converted directly to N-acetylanthranilic acid by a mild hydrolytic reaction.

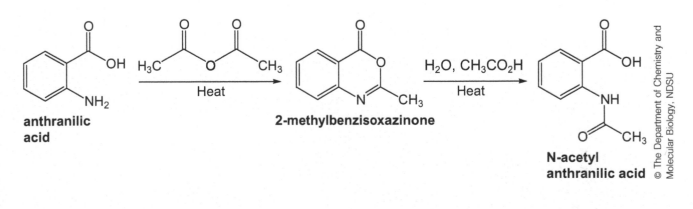

anthranilic acid → 2-methylbenzisoxazinone → N-acetyl anthranilic acid

[1] Wolff, G., Gross, G., and Stranski, I. N., *Z. Elektrochem.*, 56, 420-8 (1952).

[2] Helmkamp G. K., and Johnson, H. W., "Selected Experiments in Organic Chemistry" (2nd ed.), W. H. Freeman and Company, 1968, p. 155.

[3] Bogert M. T., and Seil, H. A., *J. Amer. Chem. Soc.*, 29, 517 (1907).

PROCEDURE

Preparation of N-acetylanthranilic acid: Place 5 g of anthranilic acid in a 100 mL round bottom flask with boiling stones and equipped with a reflux condenser. Add 15 mL of acetic anhydride, bring the mixture slowly to the reflux temperature and maintain heat for 15 min. Allow the solution to cool and add 5 mL water through the condenser. Bring the mixture to a soft boil once more and allow to cool slowly. Isolate the crystals of N-acetylanthranilic acid by suction filtration and wash the product with a small amount of cold methanol. Triturate the crystals and suspend them into hexane, then filter by suction again. Transfer the crystals to a watch glass and allow them to dry thoroughly in an oven (120°C) for 10 minutes. This procedure usually yields well-formed crystals but the material may be recrystallized from acetic acid/water mixtures.

To demonstrate the property of triboluminescence, the crystals should be well formed and it is vital that they be completely free of solvent. The triboluminescence is best demonstrated by crushing the crystals between two nesting watch glasses. The light emitted is readily observed in a darkened room.

Tetraphenylcyclopentadienone

*Prepared by Donald L. Pavia, Gary M. Lampman and George S. Kriz, Western
Washington University, and Richard Engel, Edmonds Community College*

INTRODUCTION

In this experiment, tetraphenylcyclopentadienone will be prepared by the
reaction of dibenzyl ketone (1,3-diphenyl-2-propanone) with benzil in the
presence of base.

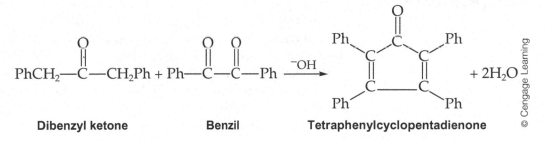

Dibenzyl ketone   **Benzil**   **Tetraphenylcyclopentadienone**

This reaction proceeds via an aldol condensation reaction, with dehydration giving the purple unsaturated cyclic ketone. A stepwise mechanism
for the reaction may proceed as follows.

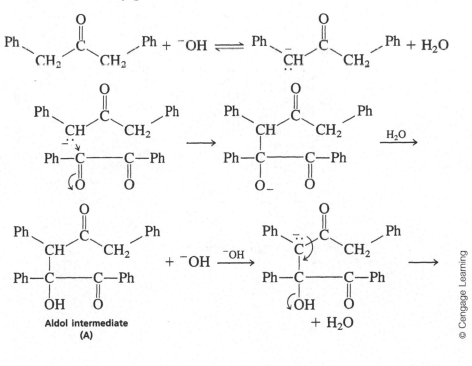

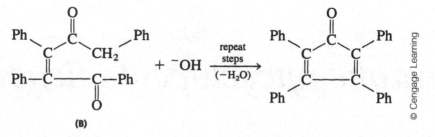

(B)

The aldol intermediate **A** readily loses water to give the highly conjugated system B, which reacts further to form a ring by an intramolecular aldol condensation. After a dehydration step (loss of water), the dienone product is formed.

PROCEDURE

Running the Reaction

Add 1.5 g of benzil, 1.5 g of dibenzyl ketone (1,3-diphenyl-2-propanone, 1,3-diphenylacetone), and 12 mL of absolute ethanol to a 50-mL round-bottom flask. Place a magnetic stir bar in the flask. Attach the condenser to the round-bottom flask. Prepare a hot water bath at 70°C. Heat the mixture in the water bath with stirring until the solids dissolve.

Raise the temperature of the hot water bath to about 80°C. Continue to stir the mixture. Using a Pasteur pipet, add dropwise 2.25 mL of ethanolic potassium hydroxide solution[1] downward through the condenser into the flask.

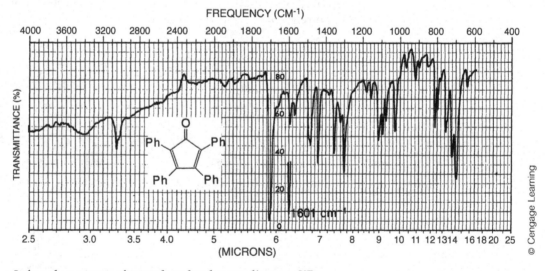

Infrared spectrum of tetraphenylcyclopentadienone, KBr.

---

[1]Note to the Instructor: This solution is prepared by dissolving 6 g of potassium hydroxide in 60 mL of absolute ethanol. It will take about 30 minutes, with vigorous stirring, for the solid to dissolve. As the solid dissolves, crush the pieces with a spatula to aid in the solution process. This will provide enough solution for 20 students, assuming little material is wasted.

Foaming may occur.

The mixture will immediately turn deep purple. Once you add the potassium hydroxide, raise the temperature of the hot water bath to about 85°C. Heat the mixture with stirring for 15 minutes.

Isolation of Product

At the end of the heating period, remove the flask from the hot water bath. Allow the mixture to cool to room temperature. Then place the flask in an ice-water bath for 5 minutes to complete crystallization of the product. Collect the deep purple crystals on a Büchner funnel. Wash the crystals with three 4-mL portions of cold 95% ethanol. The rinse solvent can also be used to aid in transferring crystals from the round-bottom flask to the Büchner funnel. Dry the tetraphenylcyclopentadienone in an oven for 15 minutes.

Yield Calculation and Melting Point Determination

Weigh the product and calculate the percentage yield. Determine the melting point. A small portion may be recrystallized, if desired, from a 1:1 mixture of 95% ethanol and toluene (12 mL/0.5 g). At the instructor's option, determine the infrared spectrum of tetraphenylcyclopentadienone in potassium bromide.

QUESTIONS

1. Interpret the infrared spectrum of tetraphenylcyclopentadienone.
2. Draw the structure of the product you would expect from the reaction of benzaldehyde and acetophenone with base.
3. Suggest two possible byproducts (excluding water) of the reaction performed in class.

Isolation of Chlorophyll and Carotenoid Pigments from Spinach

Prepared by Donald L. Pavia, Gary M. Lampman and George S. Kriz, Western Washington University, and Richard Engel, Edmonds Community College

INTRODUCTION

Photosynthesis in plants takes place in organelles called **chloroplasts.** Chloroplasts contain a number of colored compounds (pigments) which fall into two categories, **chlorophylls** and **carotenoids.**

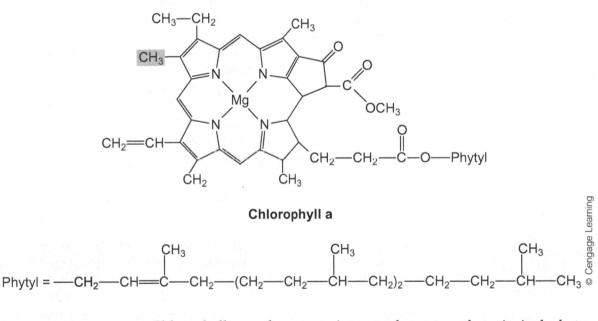

Chlorophyll a

Phytyl = $-CH_2-CH=C-CH_2-(CH_2-CH_2-CH-CH_2)_2-CH_2-CH_2-CH-CH_3$ (with CH_3 branches)

Chlorophylls are the green pigments that act as the principal photo-receptor molecules of plants. They are capable of absorbing certain wavelengths of visible light that are then converted by plants into chemical energy. Two different forms of these pigments found in plants are **chlorophyll *a*** and **chlorophyll *b*.** The two forms are identical, except that the methyl group that is shaded in the structural formula of chlorophyll *a* is replaced by a —CHO group in chlorophyll *b*. **Pheophytin *a*** and **pheophytin *b*** are identical to chlorophyll α and chlorophyll β, respectively, except that in each case the magnesium ion Mg^{2+} has been replaced by two hydrogen ions $2H^+$.

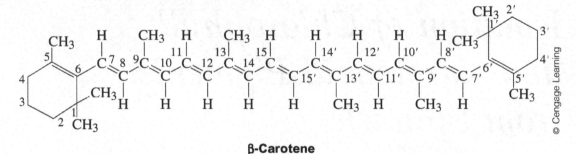

β-Carotene

Carotenoids are yellow pigments that are also involved in the photosynthetic process. In 1907, Willstätter established the structure of carotene, but it was not known until 1931–1933 that there were actually three isomers of carotene. The α-carotene differs from β-carotene in that the α isomer has a double bond between C_4 and C_5 rather than between C_5 and C_6, as in the β isomer. The γ isomer has only one ring, identical to the ring in the β isomer, whereas the other ring is opened in the γ form between C_1' and C_6'. The β isomer is by far the most common of the three. In addition, chloroplasts also contain several oxygen-containing derivatives of carotenes, called **xanthophylls.**

In this experiment, you will extract the chlorophyll and carotenoid pigments from spinach leaves using acetone as the solvent. The pigments will be separated by column chromatography using alumina as the adsorbent. Increasingly more polar solvents will be used to elute the various components from the column. The colored fractions collected will then be analyzed using thin-layer chromatography. It should be possible for you to identify most of the pigments already discussed on your thin-layer plate after development.

SPECIAL INSTRUCTIONS

Hexane and acetone are both highly flammable. Avoid the use of flames while working with these solvents. Perform the thin-layer chromatography in the hood. The procedure calls for a centrifuge tube with a tight-fitting cap. If this is not available, you can use a vortex mixer for mixing the liquids. Another alternative is to use a cork to stopper the tube; however, the cork will absorb some liquid.

Fresh spinach is preferable to frozen spinach. Because of handling, frozen spinach contains additional pigments that are difficult to identify. Since the pigments are light-sensitive and can undergo air oxidation, you should work quickly. Samples should be stored in closed containers and kept in the dark when possible. The column chromatography procedure takes less than 15 minutes to perform and cannot be stopped until it is completed. It is very important, therefore, that you have all the materials needed for this part of the experiment prepared in advance and that you are thoroughly familiar with the procedure before running the column. If you need to prepare the 70% hexane-30% acetone solvent mixture, be sure to mix it thoroughly before using.

PROCEDURE

Part A. Extraction of the Pigments

Weigh about 0.5 g of fresh (or 0.25 g of frozen) spinach leaves (avoid using stems or thick veins). Fresh spinach is preferable, if available. If you must use frozen spinach, dry the thawed leaves by pressing them between several layers of paper towels. Cut or tear the spinach leaves into small pieces and place them in a mortar along with 1.0 mL of cold acetone. Grind with a pestle until the spinach leaves have been broken into particles too small to be seen clearly. If too much acetone has evaporated, you may need to add an additional portion of acetone (0.5–1.0 mL) to perform the following step. Using a Pasteur pipet, transfer the mixture to a centrifuge tube. Rinse the mortar and pestle with 1.0 mL of cold acetone and transfer the remaining mixture to the centrifuge tube. Centrifuge the mixture (be sure to balance the centrifuge). Using a Pasteur pipet, transfer the liquid to a centrifuge tube with a tight-fitting cap (see "Special Instructions," if one is not available).

Add 2.0 mL of hexane to the tube, cap the tube, and shake the mixture thoroughly. Then, add 2.0 mL of water and shake thoroughly with occasional venting. Centrifuge the mixture to break the emulsion, which usually appears as a cloudy, green layer in the middle of the mixture. Remove the bottom aqueous layer with a Pasteur pipet. Using a Pasteur pipet, prepare a column containing anhydrous sodium sulfate to dry the remaining hexane layer, which contains the dissolved pigments. Place a plug of cotton into a Pasteur pipet ($5\frac{3}{4}$-inch) and tamp it into position using a glass rod. The correct position of the cotton is shown in the figure. Add about 0.5 g of powdered or granular anhydrous sodium sulfate and tap the column with your finger to pack the material.

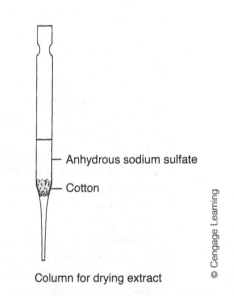

Anhydrous sodium sulfate

Cotton

Column for drying extract

© Cengage Learning

Clamp the column in a vertical position and place a dry test tube (13 × 100-mm) under the bottom of the column. Label this test tube with an E for extract so that you don't confuse it with the test tubes you will be working with later in this experiment. With a Pasteur pipet, transfer the hexane layer to the column. When all the solution has drained, add 0.5 mL of hexane to the column to extract all the pigments from the drying agent. Evaporate the solvent by placing the test tube in a warm water bath. Dissolve the residue in 0.5 mL of hexane. Stopper the test tube and place it in your drawer until you are ready to run the alumina chromatography column.

Part B. Column Chromatography

Introduction

The pigments are separated on a column packed with alumina. Although there are many different components in your sample, they usually separate into two main bands on the column. The first band to pass through the column is yellow and consists of the carotenes. This band may be less than 1 mm wide and it may pass through the column very rapidly. It is easy to miss seeing the band as it passes through the alumina. The second band consists of all the other pigments discussed in the introduction to this experiment. Although it consists of both green and yellow pigments, it appears as a green band on the column. The green band spreads out on the column more than the yellow band and it moves more slowly. Occasionally, the yellow and green components in this band will separate as the band moves down the column. If this begins to occur, you should change to a solvent of higher polarity so that they come out as one band. As the samples elute from the column, collect the yellow band (carotenes) in one test tube and the green band in another test tube.

Because the moisture content of the alumina is difficult to control, different samples of alumina may have different activities. The activity of the alumina is an important factor in determining the polarity of the solvent required to elute each band of pigments. Several solvents with a range of polarities are used in this experiment. The solvents and their relative polarities follow:

Hexane

70% hexane–30% acetone

Acetone

80% acetone–20% methanol

increasing polarity

A solvent of lower polarity elutes the yellow band; a solvent of higher polarity is required to elute the green band. In this procedure, you first try to elute the yellow band with hexane. If the yellow band does not move with hexane, you then add the next more polar solvent. Continue this process until you find a solvent that moves the yellow band. When you find the appropriate solvent, continue using it until the yellow band is eluted from the column. When the yellow band is eluted, change to the next more polar solvent. When you find a solvent that moves the green band, continue using it until the green band is eluted. Remember that occasionally a second yellow band will begin to move down the column before the green band moves. This yellow band will be much wider than the first one. If this occurs, change to a more polar solvent. This should bring all the components in the green band down at the same time.

Advance Preparation

Before running the column, assemble the following glassware and liquids. Obtain five dry test tubes and number them 1 through 5. Prepare two dry Pasteur pipets with bulbs attached. Calibrate one of them to deliver a volume of about 0.25 mL. Place 10.0 mL of hexane, 6.0 mL of 70% hexane-30% acetone solution (by volume), 6.0 mL of acetone, and 6.0 mL of 80% acetone-20% methanol (by volume) into four separate containers. Clearly label each container.

Prepare a chromatography column packed with alumina. Place a *loose* plug of cotton in a Pasteur pipet and push it *gently* into position using a glass rod (see figure on p. 59 for the correct position of the cotton). Add a small layer of sand on top of the cotton to provide a level surface. Add 1.25 g of alumina to the pipet while tapping the column gently with your finger. When all the alumina has been added, tap the column with your finger for several seconds to ensure that the alumina is tightly packed. Clamp the column in a vertical position so that the bottom of the column is just above the height of the test tubes you will be using to collect the fractions. Place test tube 1 under the column.

NOTE: Read the following procedure on running the column. The chromatography procedure takes less than 15 minutes, and you cannot stop until all the material is eluted from the column. You must have a good understanding of the whole procedure before running the column.

Running the Column

Using a Pasteur pipet, slowly add about 3.0 mL of hexane to the column. The column must be completely moistened by the solvent. Drain the excess hexane until the level of hexane reaches the top of the alumina. Once you have added hexane to the alumina, the top of the column must not be allowed to run dry. If necessary, add more hexane.

NOTE: It is essential that the liquid level not be allowed to drain below the surface of the alumina at any point during the procedure.

When the level of the hexane reaches the top of the alumina, add about 0.5 mL of the dissolved pigments to the column. Leave the remainder in the test tube for the thin-layer chromatography procedure. (Put a stopper on the tube and place it back in your drawer). Continue collecting the eluent in test tube 1. Just as the pigment solution penetrates the column, add 1 mL of hexane and drain until the surface of the liquid has reached the alumina.

Add about 4 mL of hexane. If the yellow band begins to separate from the green band, continue to add hexane until the yellow band passes through the column. If the yellow band does not separate from the green band, change to the next more polar solvent (70% hexane–30% acetone). When changing solvents, do not add the new solvent until the last solvent has nearly penetrated the alumina. When the appropriate solvent is found, add this solvent until the yellow band passes through the column. Just before the yellow band reaches the bottom of the column, place test tube 2 under the column. When the eluent becomes colorless again, place test tube 3 under the column.

Add several mL of the next more polar solvent when the level of the last solvent is almost at the top of the alumina. If the green band moves down the column, continue to add this solvent until the green band is eluted from the column. If the green band does not move or if a diffuse yellow band begins to move, change to the next more polar solvent. Change solvents again if necessary. Collect the green band in test tube 4.

When there is little or no green color in the eluent, place test tube 5 under the column and stop the procedure.

Using a warm water bath (60–80°C), evaporate the solvent from the tube containing the yellow band (tube 2), the tube containing the green band (tube 4), and the tube containing the original pigment solution (tube E). As soon as all the solvent has evaporated from each of the tubes, remove them from the water bath. Do not allow any of the tubes to remain in the water bath after the solvent has evaporated. Stopper the tubes and place them in your drawer.

Part C. Thin-Layer Chromatography

Preparing the TLC Plate

These plates have a flexible backing but should not be bent excessively. Handle them carefully, or the adsorbent may flake off them. Also, you should handle them only by the edges; the surface should not be touched. Using a lead pencil (not a pen) *lightly* draw a line across the plate (short dimension) about 1 cm from the bottom (see figure). Using a centimeter ruler, move its index about 0.6 cm in from the edge of the plate and lightly mark off three 1-cm intervals on the line. These are the points at which the samples will be spotted.

Prepare three micropipets to spot the plate. Prepare a TLC development chamber with 70% hexane–30% acetone. A beaker covered with aluminum foil or a wide-mouth screwcap bottle is a suitable container to use.

Using a Pasteur pipet, add two drops of 70% hexane–30% acetone to each of the three test tubes containing dried pigments. Swirl the tubes so that the drops of solvent dissolve as much of the pigments as possible. The TLC plate should be spotted with three samples: the extract, the yellow band from the column, and the green band. For each of the three samples, use a different micropipet to spot the sample on the plate. Take up part of the sample in the pipet (don't use a bulb; capillary action will draw up

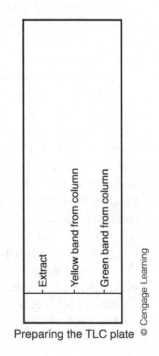

Preparing the TLC plate © Cengage Learning

the liquid). For the extract (tube labeled E) and the green band (tube 4), touch the plate once *lightly* and let the solvent evaporate. The spot should be no longer than 2 mm in diameter and should be a fairly dark green. For the yellow band (tube 2), repeat the spotting technique 5–10 times, until the spot is a definite yellow color. Allow the solvent to evaporate completely between successive applications, and spot the plate in exactly the same position each time. Save the samples in case you need to repeat the TLC.

Developing the TLC Plate

Place the TLC plate in the development chamber. Remove the plate when the solvent front is 1–2 cm from the top of the plate. Using a lead pencil, mark the position of the solvent front. As soon as the plates have dried, outline the spots with a pencil and indicate the colors. This is important to do soon after the plates have dried, because some of the pigments will change color when exposed to the air.

Analysis of the Results

In the crude extract you should be able to see the following components (in order of decreasing R_f values):

Carotenes (1 spot) (yellow-orange)

Pheophytin *a* (gray, may be nearly as intense as chlorophyll *b)*

Pheophytin *b* (gray, may not be visible)

Chlorophyll *a* (blue-green, more intense than chlorophyll *b*)

Chlorophyll *b* (green)

Xanthophylls (possibly 3 spots: yellow)

Depending on the spinach sample, the conditions of the experiment, and how much sample was spotted on the TLC plate, you may observe other pigments. These additional components can result from air oxidation, hydrolysis, or other chemical reactions involving the pigments discussed in this experiment. It is very common to observe other pigments in samples of frozen spinach. It is also common to observe components in the green band that were not present in the extract.

Identify as many of the spots in your samples as possible. Determine which pigments were present in the yellow band and in the green band. Draw a picture of the TLC plate in your notebook. Label each spot with its color and its identity, where possible. Additionally, visualize the spots on your TLC plate using both ultraviolet light and iodine staining. Calculate the R_f values for each spot produced by chromatography of the extract.

QUESTIONS

1. Why are the chlorophylls less mobile on column chromatography and why do they have lower R_f values than the carotenes?

2. Propose structural formulas for pheophytin *a* and pheophytin *b*.

3. What would happen to the R_f values of the pigments if you were to increase the relative concentration of acetone in the developing solvent?

4. Using your results as a guide, comment on the purity of the material in the green and yellow bands.

Sulfa Drugs: Preparation of Sulfanilamide

Prepared by Donald L. Pavia, Gary M. Lampman and George S. Kriz, Western Washington University, and Richard Engel, Edmonds Community College

SULFA DRUGS

The history of chemotherapy extends as far back as 1909 when Paul Ehrlich first used the term. Although Ehrlich's original definition of chemotherapy was limited, he is recognized as one of the giants of medicinal chemistry. **Chemotherapy** might be defined as "the treatment of disease by chemical reagents." It is preferable that these chemical reagents exhibit a toxicity toward only the pathogenic organism, and not toward both the organism and the host. A chemotherapeutic agent would not be useful if it poisoned the patient at the same time that it cured the patient's disease!

In 1932, the German dye manufacturing firm I. G. Farbenindustrie patented a new drug, Prontosil. Prontosil is a red azo dye, and it was first prepared for its dye properties. Remarkably, it was discovered that Prontosil showed antibacterial action when it was used to dye wool. This discovery led to studies of Prontosil as a drug capable of inhibiting the growth of bacteria. The following year, Prontosil was successfully used against staphylococcal septicemia, a blood infection. In 1935, Gerhard Domagk published the results of his research, which indicated that Prontosil was capable of curing streptococcal infections of mice and rabbits. Prontosil was shown to be active against a wide variety of bacteria in later work. This important discovery, which paved the way for a tremendous amount of research on the chemotherapy of bacterial infections, earned for Domagk the 1939 Nobel Prize in Medicine, but an order from Hitler prevented Domagk from accepting the honor.

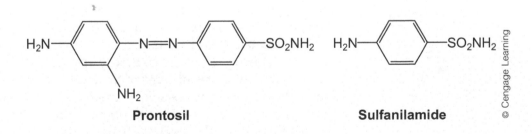

Prontosil   **Sulfanilamide**

Prontosil is an effective antibacterial substance **in vivo,** that is, when injected into a living animal. Prontosil is not medicinally active when the drug is tested **in vitro,** that is, on a bacterial culture grown in the laboratory. In 1935, the research group at the Pasteur Institute in Paris headed by J. Tréfouël learned that Prontosil is metabolized in animals to **sulfanilamide.** Sulfanilamide had been known since 1908. Experiments with sulfanilamide showed that it had the same action as Prontosil in vivo and that it was also active in vitro, where Prontosil was known to be inactive. It was concluded that the active portion of the Prontosil molecule was the sulfanilamide moiety. This discovery led to an explosion of interest in sulfonamide derivatives. Well over a thousand sulfonamide substances were prepared within a few years of these discoveries.

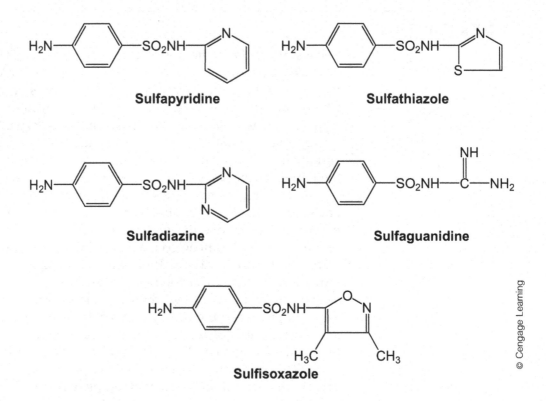

Sulfapyridine   **Sulfathiazole**

Sulfadiazine   **Sulfaguanidine**

Sulfisoxazole

© Cengage Learning

Although many sulfonamide compounds were prepared, only a relative few showed useful antibacterial properties. As the first useful antibacterial drugs, these few medicinally active sulfonamides, or **sulfa drugs,** became the wonder drugs of their day. An antibacterial drug may be either **bacteriostatic** or **bactericidal.** A bacteriostatic drug suppresses the growth of bacteria; a bactericidal drug kills bacteria. Strictly speaking, the sulfa drugs are bacteriostatic. The structures of some of the most common sulfa drugs are shown here. These more complex sulfa drugs have various important applications. Although they do not have the simple structure characteristic of sulfanilamide, they tend to be less toxic than the simpler compound.

Sulfa drugs began to lose their importance as generalized antibacterial agents when production of antibiotics in large quantity began. In 1929, Sir Alexander Fleming made his famous discovery of **penicillin.** In 1941, penicillin was first used successfully on humans. Since that time, the study of antibiotics has spread to molecules that bear little or no structural similarity to the sulfonamides. Besides penicillin derivatives, antibiotics that are derivatives of **tetracycline,** including Aureomycin and Terramycin, were also discovered. These newer antibiotics have high activity against bacteria, and they do not usually have the severe unpleasant side effects of many of the sulfa drugs. Nevertheless, the sulfa drugs are still widely used in treating malaria, tuberculosis, leprosy, meningitis, pneumonia, scarlet fever, plague, respiratory infections, and infections of the intestinal and urinary tracts.

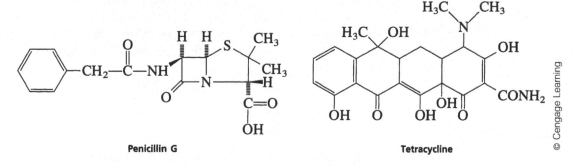

Penicillin G   Tetracycline

Even though the importance of sulfa drugs has declined, studies of how these materials act provide very interesting insights into how chemo-therapeutic substances might behave. In 1940, Woods and Fildes discovered that *p*-aminobenzoic acid (PABA) inhibits the action of sulfanilamide. They concluded that sulfanilamide and PABA, because of their structural similar-ity, must compete with each other within the organism even though they cannot carry out the same chemical function. Further studies indicated that sulfanilamide does not kill bacteria but inhibits their growth. In order to grow, bacteria require an enzyme-catalyzed reaction that uses **folic acid** as a cofactor. Bacteria synthesize folic acid, using PABA as one of the components. When sulfanilamide is introduced into the bacterial cell, it competes with PABA for the active site of the enzyme that carries out the incorporation of PABA into the molecule of folic acid. Because sulfanilamide and PABA compete for an active site due to their structural similarity and because sul-fanilamide cannot carry out the chemical transformations characteristic of PABA once it has formed a complex with the enzyme, sulfanilamide is called a **competitive inhibitor** of the enzyme. The enzyme, once it has formed a complex with sulfanilamide, is incapable of catalyzing the reaction required for the synthesis of folic acid. Without folic acid, the bacteria cannot syn-thesize the nucleic acids required for growth. As a result, bacterial growth is arrested until the body's immune system can respond and kill the bacteria.

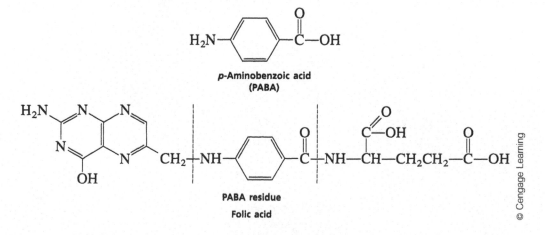

p-Aminobenzoic acid
(PABA)

PABA residue

Folic acid

One might well ask the question, "Why, when someone takes sulfanilamide as a drug, doesn't it inhibit the growth of *all* cells, bacterial and human alike?" The answer is simple. Animal cells cannot synthesize folic acid. Folic acid must be a part of the diet of animals and is therefore an essential vitamin. Since animal cells receive their fully synthesized folic acid molecules through the diet, only the bacterial cells are affected by the sulfanilamide, and only their growth is inhibited.

For most drugs, a detailed picture of their mechanism of action is unavailable. The sulfa drugs, however, provide a rare example from which we can theorize how other therapeutic agents carry out their medicinal activity.

REFERENCES

Amundsen, L. H. "Sulfanilamide and Related Chemotherapeutic Agents." *Journal of Chemical Education,* *19* (1942): 167.

Evans, R. M. *The Chemistry of Antibiotics Used in Medicine.* London: Pergamon Press, 1965.

Fieser, L. F., and Fieser, M. *Topics in Organic Chemistry.* New York: Reinhold, 1963. Chap. 7, "Chemotherapy."

Garrod, L. P., and O'Grady, F. *Antibiotic and Chemotherapy.* Edinburgh: E. and S. Livingstone, Ltd., 1968.

Goodman, L. S., and Gilman, A. *The Pharmacological Basis of Therapeutics.* 8th ed. New York: Pergamon Press, 1990. Chap. 45, "The Sulfonamides," by G. L. Mandell and M. A. Sande.

Sementsov, A. "The Medical Heritage from Dyes." *Chemistry,* *39* (November 1966): 20.

Zahner, H. and Maas, W. K. *Biology of Antibiotics.* Berlin: Springer-Verlag, 1972.

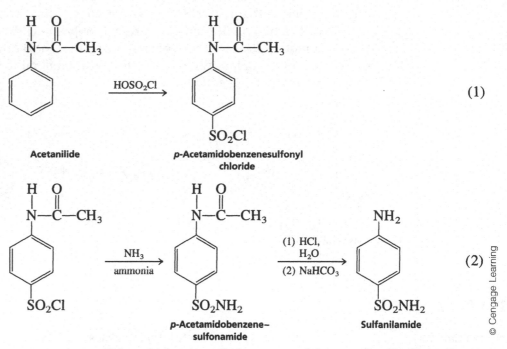

(1)

(2)

p-Acetamidobenzene–sulfonamide

Sulfanilamide

Acetanilide, which can easily be prepared from aniline, is allowed to react with chlorosulfonic acid to yield *p*-acetamidobenzenesulfonyl chloride. The acetamido group directs substitution almost totally to the *para* position. The reaction is an example of an electrophilic aromatic substitution reaction. Two problems would result if aniline itself were used in the reaction. First, the amino group in aniline would be protonated in strong acid to become a *meta* director; and, second, the chlorosulfonic acid would react with the amino group rather than with the ring, to give C_6H_5—$NHSO_3H$. For these reasons, the amino group has been "protected" by acetylation. The acetyl group will be removed in the final step, after it is no longer needed, to regenerate the free amino group present in sulfanilamide.

p-Acetamidobenzenesulfonyl chloride is isolated by adding the reaction mixture to ice water, which decomposes the excess chlorosulfonic acid. This intermediate is fairly stable in water; nevertheless, it is converted slowly to the corresponding sulfonic acid (Ar—SO_3H). Thus, it should be isolated as soon as possible from the aqueous medium by filtration.

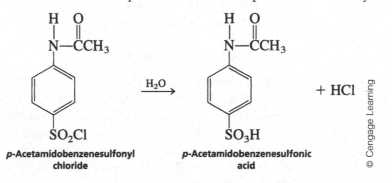

p-Acetamidobenzenesulfonyl chloride

p-Acetamidobenzenesulfonic acid

The intermediate sulfonyl chloride is converted to *p*-acetamidobenzenesulfonamide by a reaction with aqueous ammonia (Step 2). Excess ammonia neutralizes the hydrogen chloride produced. The only side reaction is the hydrolysis of the sulfonyl chloride to *p*-acetamidobenzenesulfonic acid.

The protecting acetyl group is removed by acid-catalyzed hydrolysis to generate the hydrochloride salt of the product, sulfanilamide. Notice that of the two amide linkages present, only the carboxylic acid amide (acet-amido group) was cleaved, not the sulfonic acid amide (sulfonamide). The salt of the sulfa drug is converted to sulfanilamide when the base, sodium bicarbonate, is added.

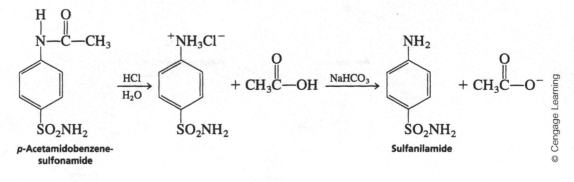

© Cengage Learning

PROCEDURE

Sulfanilamide

Preparation of p-*Acetamidobenzenesulfonamide*

In a hood, prepare a hot water bath at 70°C using a 250-mL beaker. Place 2.5 g p-acetamidobenzenesulfonyl chloride into a 50-mL Erlenmeyer flask and add 11 mL of dilute ammonium hydroxide solution.[1] Stir the mixture well with a stirring rod to break up the lumps. Heat the mixture in the hot water bath for 10 minutes, stirring occasionally. Allow the flask to cool to the touch and place it in an ice water bath for several minutes. Collect the p-acetamidobenzenesulfonamide on a Büchner funnel and rinse the flask and product with about 10 mL of ice water.

Hydrolysis of p-*Acetamidobenzenesulfonamide*

Transfer the solid into a 25-mL round-bottom flask and add 5.3 mL of dilute hydrochloric acid solution[2] and a boiling stone. Attach a reflux condenser to the flask. Using a heating mantle, heat the mixture under reflux until the solid has dissolved (about 10 minutes) and then reflux for an additional 5 minutes. Allow the mixture to cool to room temperature. If a solid (unreacted starting material) appears, bring the mixture to a boil again for several minutes. When the flask has cooled to room temperature, no further solids should appear.

Isolation of Sulfanilamide

With a Pasteur pipet transfer the solution to a 100-mL beaker. While stirring with a glass rod, cautiously add dropwise aqueous saturated sodium bicarbonate to the mixture in the beaker. Foaming will occur after each addition of the bicarbonate mixture because of carbon dioxide evolution. Allow gas evolution to cease before making the next addition. Eventually, sulfanilamide will begin to precipitate. At this point, begin to check the pH of the solution. Add the aqueous sodium bicarbonate until the pH of the solution is between 4 and 6. Cool the mixture thoroughly in an ice water

---

[1] Prepared by mixing 110 mL of concentrated ammonium hydroxide with 110 mL of water.

[2] Prepared by mixing 70 mL of water with 36 mL of concentrated hydrochloric acid.

bath. Collect the sulfanilamide on a Büchner funnel and rinse the beaker and solid with about 5 mL of cold water. Allow the solid to air-dry on the Büchner funnel for several minutes using suction. Dry the sulfanilamide in your drawer until the next laboratory class.

Yield Calculation, Melting Point, and Infrared Spectrum

Weigh the dry sulfanilamide and calculate the percentage yield. Determine the melting point and obtain the infrared spectrum in potassium bromide (Figure 1).

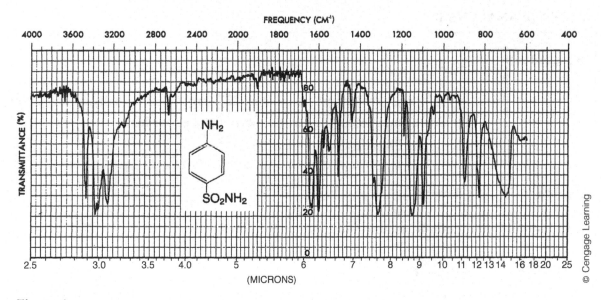

Figure 1
Infrared spectrum of sulfanilamide, KBr

QUESTIONS

1. Write an equation showing how excess chlorosulfonic acid is decomposed in water.

2. In the preparation of sulfanilamide, why was aqueous sodium bicarbonate, rather than aqueous sodium hydroxide, used to neutralize the solution in the final step?

3. At first glance, it might seem possible to prepare sulfanilamide from sulfanilic acid by the set of reactions shown here.

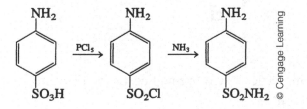

When the reaction is conducted in this way, however, a polymeric product is produced after the first step. What is the structure of the polymer? Why does *p*-acetamidobenzenesulfonyl chloride not produce a polymer?

SULFUR COMPOUNDS

Infrared spectral data for sulfur-containing compounds are covered in this section. Included here are single-bonded compounds (mercaptans or thiols and sulfides). Double-bonded S=O compounds are also included in this section.

SPECTRAL ANALYSIS BOX

Mercaptans   **R—S—H**

S—H   Stretch, one weak band, occurs near 2550 cm^{-1} and virtually confirms the presence of this group, since few other absorptions appear here.

Example: benzenethiol (Figure 2).

Sulfides   **R—S—R**

Little useful information is obtained from the infrared spectrum.

Sulfoxides   **R—S—R**
                                   ║
                                   O

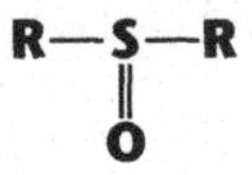

S=O   Stretch, one strong band, occurs near 1050 cm^{-1}.

Sulfones   **O**
                               ║
                         R—S—R
                               ║
                               O

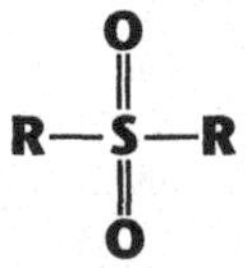

S=O   Asymmetric stretch (strong) occurs at 1300 cm^{-1}, symmetric stretch (strong) at 1150 cm^{-1}.

Sulfonyl Chlorides   **O**
                                           ║
                                    R—S—Cl
                                         ║
                                         O

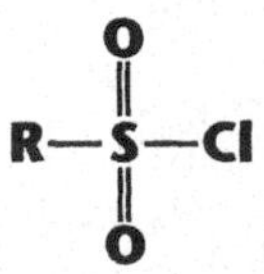

S=O   Asymmetric stretch (strong) occurs at 1375 cm^{-1}, symmetric stretch (strong) at 1185 cm^{-1}.

Example: benzenesulfonyl chloride (Figure 3).

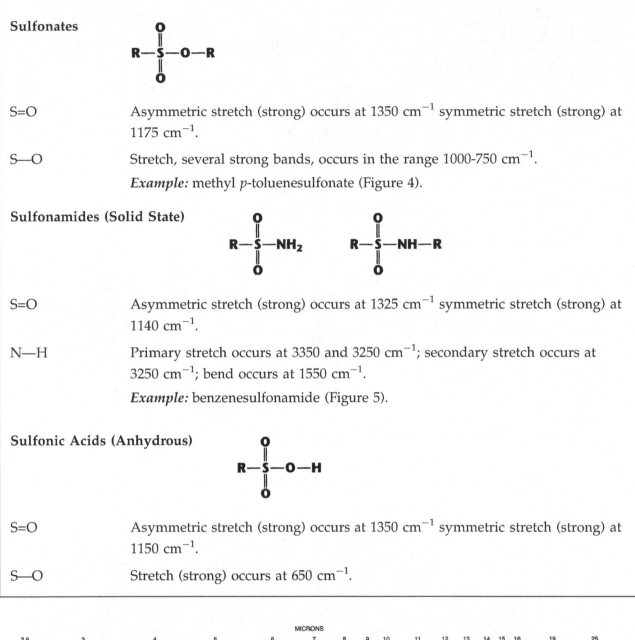

Sulfonates

S=O   Asymmetric stretch (strong) occurs at 1350 cm^{-1} symmetric stretch (strong) at 1175 cm^{-1}.

S—O   Stretch, several strong bands, occurs in the range 1000-750 cm^{-1}.

Example: methyl *p*-toluenesulfonate (Figure 4).

Sulfonamides (Solid State)

S=O   Asymmetric stretch (strong) occurs at 1325 cm^{-1} symmetric stretch (strong) at 1140 cm^{-1}.

N—H   Primary stretch occurs at 3350 and 3250 cm^{-1}; secondary stretch occurs at 3250 cm^{-1}; bend occurs at 1550 cm^{-1}.

Example: benzenesulfonamide (Figure 5).

Sulfonic Acids (Anhydrous)

S=O   Asymmetric stretch (strong) occurs at 1350 cm^{-1} symmetric stretch (strong) at 1150 cm^{-1}.

S—O   Stretch (strong) occurs at 650 cm^{-1}.

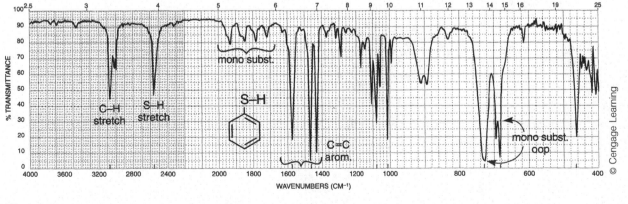

Figure 2

The infrared spectrum of benzenethiol (neat liquid, KBr plates)

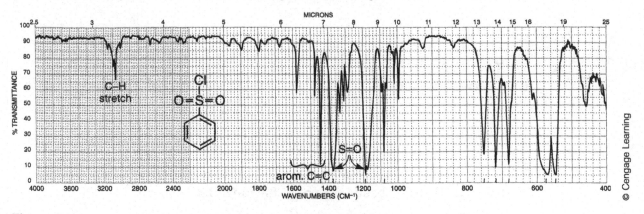

Figure 3

The infrared spectrum of benzenesulfonyl chloride (neat liquid, KBr plates)

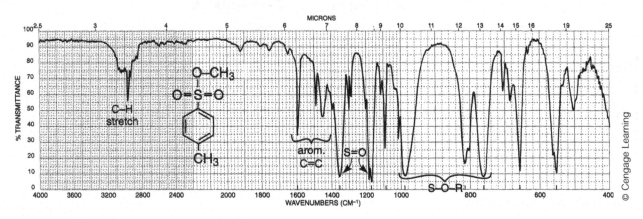

Figure 4

The infrared spectrum of methyl p-toluenesulfonate (neat liquid, KBr plates)

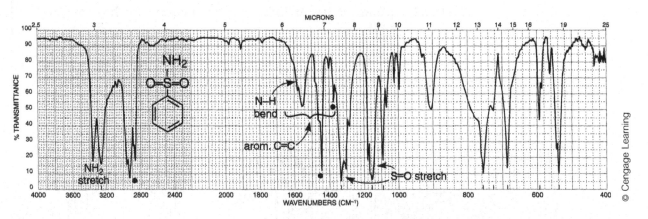

Figure 5

The infrared spectrum of benzenesulfonamide (Nujol mull, KBr plates); dots indicate the Nujol (mineral oil) absorption bands

N,N-Diethyl-*m*-Toluamide:
The Insect Repellent OFF®

Prepared by Donald L. Pavia, Gary M. Lampman and George S. Kriz, Western Washington University, and Richard Engel, Edmonds Community College

PHEROMONES: INSECT ATTRACTANTS AND REPELLENTS

It is difficult for humans, who are accustomed to heavy reliance on visual and verbal forms of communication, to imagine that there are forms of life that depend primarily on the release and perception of **odors** to communicate with one another. Among insects, however, this is perhaps the chief form of communication. Many species of insects have developed a virtual "language" based on the exchange of odors. These insects have well-developed scent glands, often of several different types, which have as their sole purpose the synthesis and release of chemical substances. When these chemical substances, known as **pheromones,** are secreted by insects and detected by other members of the same species, they induce a specific and characteristic response. Pheromones are usually of two distinct types: releaser pheromones and primer pheromones. **Releaser pheromones** produce an immediate **behavioral** response in the recipient insect; **primer pheromones** trigger a series of **physiological** changes in the recipient. Some pheromones, however, combine both releaser and primer effects.

Sex Attractants

Among the most important types of releaser pheromones are the sex attractants. **Sex attractants** are pheromones secreted by either the female or, less commonly, the male of the species to attract the opposite member for the purpose of mating. In large concentrations, sex pheromones also induce a physiological response in the recipient (for example, the changes necessary to the mating act), and thus have a primer effect and so are misnamed.

Anyone who has owned a female cat or dog knows that sex pheromones are not limited to insects. Female cats or dogs widely advertise, by odor, their sexual availability when they are "in heat." This type of pheromone is not uncommon to mammals. Some persons even believe that there are human pheromones responsible for attracting certain sensitive males and females to one another. This idea is, of course, responsible for many of the perfumes and fragrances now widely available. Whether or not the idea is correct cannot yet be established, but there are proven sexual differences in the ability of humans to smell certain substances.

For instance, Exaltolide, a synthetic lactone of 14-hydroxy-tetradecanoic acid, can be perceived only by females or by males after they have been injected with an estrogen. Exaltolide is very similar in overall structure to civetone (civet cat) and muskone (musk deer), which are two naturally occurring compounds believed to be mammalian sex pheromones. Whether human males emit pheromones has never been established. Curiously, Exaltolide is used in fragrances intended for female as well as male use! But while the odor may lead a woman to believe that she smells pleasant, it cannot possibly have any effect on the male. The "musk oils," civetone and muskone, have also been long used in expensive perfumes.

One of the first identified insect attractants belongs to the gypsy moth, *Lymantria dispar*. This moth is a common agricultural pest, and it was hoped that the sex attractant that females emitted could be used to lure and trap males. Such a method of insect control would be preferable to inundating large areas with DDT and would be species-specific. Nearly 50 years of work were expended in identifying the chemical substance responsible. Early in this period, researchers found that an extract from the tail sections of female gypsy moths would attract males, even from a great distance. In experiments with the isolated gypsy moth pheromone, it was found that the male gypsy moth has an almost unbelievable ability to detect extremely small amounts of the substance. He can detect it in concentrations lower than a few hundred *molecules* per cubic centimeter (about 10^{-19}–10^{-20} g/cc)! When a male moth encounters a small concentration of pheromone, he immediately turns into the wind and flies upward in search of higher concentrations and the female. In only a mild breeze, a continuously emitting female can activate a space 300 ft high, 700 ft wide, and almost 14,000 ft (nearly 3 miles) long!

In subsequent work, 20 mg of a pure chemical substance was isolated from solvent extracts of the two extreme tail segments collected from each of 500,000 female gypsy moths (about 0.1 μg/moth). This emphasizes that pheromones are effective in very minute amounts and that chemists must work with very small amounts to isolate them and prove their structures. It is not unusual to process thousands of insects in order to get even a very small sample of these substances. Very sophisticated analytical and instrumental methods, like spectroscopy, must be used to determine the structure of a pheromone.

In spite of these techniques, the original researchers assigned an incorrect structure to the gypsy moth pheromone and proposed for it the name gyplure. Because of its great promise as a method of insect control, gyplure was soon synthesized. The synthetic material turned out to be totally inactive. After some controversy about why the synthetic material was incapable of luring male gypsy moths (see the references for the complete story), it was finally shown that the proposed structure for the pheromone (that is, the gyplure structure) was incorrect. The actual pheromone was found to be *cis*-7,8-epoxy-2-methyloctadecane, also named (7R,8S)-epoxy-2-methyloctadecane. This material was soon synthesized, found to be active, and given the name disparlure. In recent years, disparlure traps have been found to be a convenient and economical method for controlling the gypsy moth.

INSECT SEX ATTRACTANTS

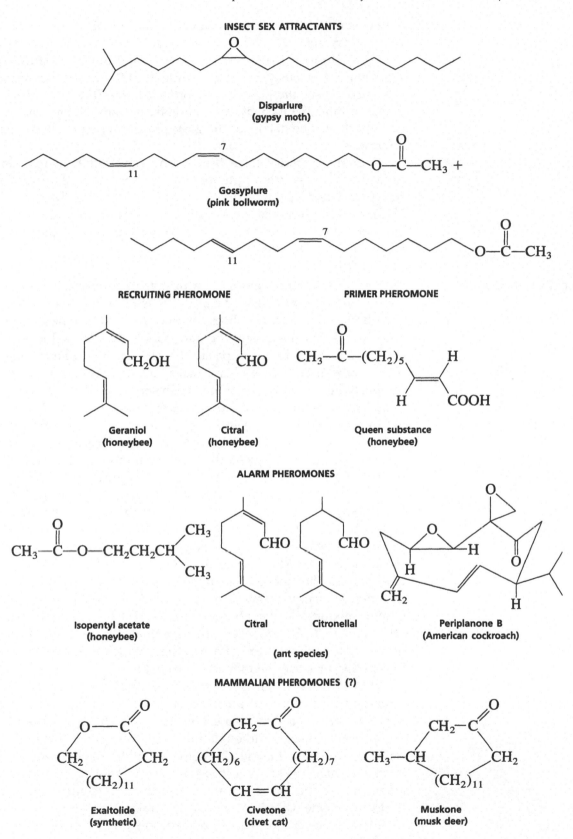

Disparlure
(gypsy moth)

Gossyplure
(pink bollworm)

RECRUITING PHEROMONE   **PRIMER PHEROMONE**

Geraniol   **Citral**   **Queen substance**
(honeybee)   **(honeybee)**   **(honeybee)**

ALARM PHEROMONES

Isopentyl acetate   **Citral**   **Citronellal**   **Periplanone B**
(honeybee)   **(American cockroach)**

(ant species)

MAMMALIAN PHEROMONES (?)

Exaltolide   **Civetone**   **Muskone**
(synthetic)   **(civet cat)**   **(musk deer)**

A similar story of mistaken identity can be related for the structure of the pheromone of the pink bollworm, *Pectinophora gossypiella*. The originally proposed structure was called propylure. Synthetic propylure turned out to be inactive. Subsequently the pheromone was shown to be a mixture of two isomers of 7,11-hexadecadien-l-yl acetate, the *cis,cis* (7Z,11Z) isomer and the *cis, trans* (7Z,11E) isomer. It turned out to be quite easy to synthesize a 1:1 mixture of these two isomers, and the 1:1 mixture was named gossyplure. Curiously, adding as little as 10% of either of the other two possible isomers, *trans,cis* (7E,11Z) or *trans,trans* (7E,11E), to the 1:1 mixture greatly diminishes its activity, apparently masking it. Stereoisomerism can be important! The details of the gossyplure story can also be found in the references.

Both these stories have been partly repeated here to point out the difficulties of research on pheromones. The usual method is to propose a structure determined by work on *very tiny* amounts of the natural material. The margin for error is great. Such proposals are usually not considered "proved" until synthetic material is shown to be as biologically effective as the natural pheromone.

Other Pheromones

The most important example of a **primer pheromone** is found in honeybees. A bee colony consists of one queen bee, several hundred male drones, and thousands of worker bees, or undeveloped females. It has recently been found that the queen, the only female that has achieved full development and reproductive capacity, secretes a primer pheromone called the **queen substance.** The worker females, while tending the queen bee, continuously ingest quantities of the queen substance. This pheromone, which is a mixture of compounds, prevents the workers from rearing any competitive queens and prevents the development of ovaries in all other females in the hive. The substance is also active as a sex attractant; it attracts drones to the queen during her "nuptial flight." The major component of queen substance is shown in the figure.

Honeybees also produce several other important types of pheromones. It has long been known that bees will swarm after an intruder. It has also been known that isopentyl acetate induces a similar behavior in bees. Isopentyl acetate is an **alarm pheromone.** When an angry worker bee stings an intruder, she discharges, along with the sting venom, a mixture of pheromones that incites the other bees to swarm upon and attack the intruder. Isopentyl acetate is an important component of the alarm pheromone mixture. Alarm pheromones have also been identified in many other insects. In insects less aggressive than bees or ants, the alarm pheromone may take the form of a **repellent,** which induces the insects to go into hiding or leave the immediate vicinity.

Honeybees also release **recruiting** or **trail pheromones.** These pheromones attract others to a source of food. Honeybees secrete recruiting pheromones when they locate flowers in which large amounts of sugar syrup are available. Although the recruiting pheromone is a complex mixture, both geraniol and citral have been identified as components. In a similar fashion, when ants locate a source of food, they drag their tails along the ground on their way back to the nest, continuously secreting a trail pheromone. Other ants follow the trail to the source of food.

In some species of insects, **recognition pheromones** have been identified. In carpenter ants, a caste-specific secretion has been found in the mandibular glands of the males of five different species. These secretions have several functions, one of which is to allow members of the same species to recognize one another. Insects not having the correct recognition odor are immediately attacked and expelled from the nest. In one species of carpenter ant, the recognition pheromone has been shown to have methyl anthranilate as an important component.

We do not yet know all the types of pheromones that any given species of insect may use, but it seems that as few as 10 or 12 pheromones could constitute a "language" that could adequately regulate the entire life cycle of a colony of social insects.

Insect Repellents

Currently, the most widely used **insect repellent** is the synthetic substance N,N-diethyl-m-toluamide, also called Deet. It is effective against fleas, mosquitoes, chiggers, ticks, deerflies, sandflies, and biting gnats. A specific repellent is known for each of these types of insects, but none has the wide spectrum of activity that this repellent has. Exactly why these substances repel insects is not yet fully understood. The most extensive investigations have been carried out on the mosquito.

Originally, many investigators thought that repellents might simply be compounds that provided unpleasant or distasteful odors to a wide variety of insects. Others thought that they might be alarm pheromones for the species affected, or that they might be the alarm pheromones of a hostile species. Early research with the mosquito indicates that at least for several varieties of mosquitoes, none of these is the correct answer.

Mosquitoes seem to have hairs on their antennae that are receptors enabling them to find a warm-blooded host. These receptors detect the convection currents arising from a warm and moist living animal. When a mosquito encounters a warm and moist convection current, it moves steadily forward. If it passes out of the current into dry air, it turns until it finds the current again. Eventually it finds the host and lands. Repellents cause a mosquito to turn in flight and become confused. Even if it should land, it becomes confused and flies away again.

Researchers have found that the repellent prevents the moisture receptors of the mosquito from responding normally to the raised humidity of the subject. At least two sensors are involved, one responsive to carbon dioxide and the other responsive to water vapor. The carbon dioxide sensor is activated by the repellent, but if exposure to the chemical continues, adaptation occurs, and the sensor returns to its usual low output of signal. The moisture sensor, on the other hand, simply seems to be deadened, or turned off, by the repellent. Therefore, mosquitoes have great difficulty in finding and interpreting a host when they are in an environment saturated with repellent. They fly right through warm and humid convection currents as if the currents did not exist. Only time will tell if other biting insects respond likewise.

REFERENCES

Agosta, W. C. "Using Chemicals to Communicate." *Journal of Chemical Education, 71* (March 1994): 242.

Batra, S. W. T. "Polyester-Making Bees and Other Innovative Insect Chemists." *Journal of Chemical Education, 62* (February 1985): 121.

Katzenellenbogen, J. A. "Insect Pheromone Synthesis: New Methodology." *Science, 194* (October 8, 1976): 139.

Leonhardt, B. A. "Pheromones." *ChemTech, 15* (June 1985): 368.

Prestwick, G. D. "The Chemical Defenses of Termites." *Scientific American, 249* (August 1983): 78.

Silverstein, R. M. "Pheromones: Background and Potential Use for Insect Control." *Science, 213* (September 18, 1981): 1326.

Stine, W. R. "Pheromones: Chemical Communication by Insects." *Journal of Chemical Education, 63* (July 1986): 603.

Villemin, D. "Olefln Oxidation: A Synthesis of Queen Bee Pheromone." *Chemistry and Industry* (January 20, 1986): 69.

Wilson, E. O. "Pheromones." *Scientific American, 208* (May 1963): 100.

Winston, M. L., and Slessor, K. N. "The Essence of Royalty: Honey Bee Queen Pheromone." *American Scientist, 80* (July–August 1992): 374.

Wood, W. F. "Chemical Ecology: Chemical Communication in Nature." *Journal of Chemical Education, 60* (July 1983): 531.

Wright, R. H. "Why Mosquito Repellents Repel." *Scientific American, 233* (July 1975): 105.

Yu, H., Becker, H., and Mangold, H. K. "Preparation of Some Pheromone Bouquets." *Chemistry and Industry* (January 16, 1989): 39.

Gypsy Moth

Beroza, M., and Knipling, E. F. "Gypsy Moth Control with the Sex Attractant Pheromone." *Science, 177* (1972): 19.

Bierl, B. A., Beroza, M., and Collier, C. W. "Potent Sex Attractant of the Gypsy Moth: Its Isolation, Identification, and Synthesis." *Science, 170* (1970): 87.

Pink Bollworm

Anderson, R. J., and Henrick, C. A. "Preparation of the Pink Bollworm Sex Pheromone Mixture, Gossyplure." *Journal of the American Chemical Society, 97* (1975): 4327.

Hummel, H. E., Gaston, L. K., Shorey, H. H., Kaae, R. S., Byrne, K. J., and Silverstein, R. M. "Clarification of the Chemical Status of the Pink Bollworm Sex Pheromone." *Science, 181* (1973): 873.

American Cockroach

Adams, M. A., Nakanishi, K., Still, W. C., Arnold, E. V., Clardy, J., and Persoon, C. J. "Sex Pheromone of the American Cockroach: Absolute Configuration of Periplanone-B." *Journal of the American Chemical Society, 101* (1979): 2495.

Still, W. C. "(±)-Periplanone-B: Total Synthesis and Structure of the Sex Excitant Pheromone of the American Cockroach." *Journal of the American Chemical Society, 101* (1979): 2493.

Stinson, S. C. "Scientists Synthesize Roach Sex Excitant." *Chemical and Engineering News, 57* (April 30, 1979): 24.

Spider

Schulz, S., and Toft, S. "Identification of a Sex Pheromone from a Spider." *Science, 260* (June 11, 1993): 1635.

Silkworm   Emsley, J. "Sex and the Discerning Silkworm." *New Scientist, 135* (July 11, 1992): 18.

Aphids   Coghlan, A. "Aphids Fall for Siren Scent of Pheromones." *New Scientist, 127* (July 21, 1990): 32.

Snakes   Mason, R. T., Fales, H. M., Jones, T. H., Pannell, L. K., Chinn, J. W., and Crews, D. "Sex Pheromones in Snakes." *Science, 245* (July 21, 1989): 290.

Oriental Fruit Moth   Mithran, S., and Mamdapur, V. R. "A Facile Synthesis of the Oriental Fruit Moth Sex Pheromone." *Chemistry and Industry* (October 20, 1986): 711.

EXPERIMENT

N, N-Diethyl-*m*-Toluamide: The Insect Repellant OFF®

Preparation of an amide

Extraction

Column chromatography

In this experiment, you will synthesize the active ingredient of the insect repellent OFF, *N,N*-diethyl-*m*-toluamide. This substance belongs to the class of compounds called **amides**. Amides have the generalized structure

$$R-\overset{\overset{\displaystyle O}{\|}}{C}-NH_2$$

The amide to be prepared in this experiment is a disubstituted amide. That is, two of the hydrogens on the amide —NH₂ group have been replaced with ethyl groups. Amides cannot be prepared directly by mixing a carboxylic acid with an amine. If an acid and an amine are mixed, an acid-base reaction occurs, giving the conjugate base of the acid, which will not react further while in solution:

$$RCOOH + R_2NH \longrightarrow [RCOO^- R_2NH_2^+]$$

However, if the amine salt is isolated as a crystalline solid and strongly heated, the amide can be prepared:

$$[RCOO^- R_2NH_2^+] \xrightarrow{\text{heat}} RCONR_2 + H_2O$$

This is not a convenient laboratory method because of the high temperature required for this reaction.

Amides are usually prepared via the acid chloride, as in this experiment. In Step 1, *m*-toluic acid is converted to its acid chloride derivative using thionyl chloride (SOCl₂).

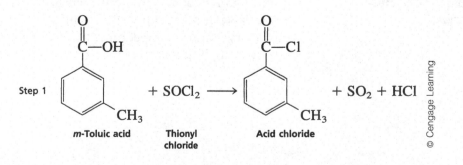

The acid chloride is not isolated or purified, and it is allowed to react directly with diethylamine in Step 2. An excess of diethylamine is used in this experiment to react with the hydrogen chloride produced in Step 2.

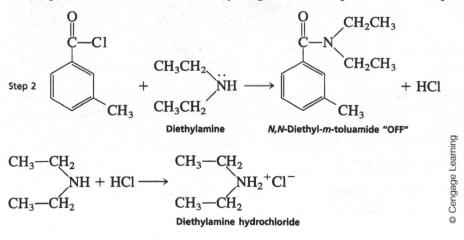

SPECIAL INSTRUCTIONS

All equipment used in this experiment should be dry, because thionyl chloride reacts with water to liberate HCl and SO_2. Likewise, *anhydrous* ether should be used, because water reacts with both thionyl chloride and the intermediate acid chloride.

Thionyl chloride is a noxious and corrosive chemical and should be handled with care. If it is spilled on the skin, serious burns will result. Thionyl chloride and diethylamine must be dispensed **in the hood** from bottles that should be kept tightly closed when not in use. Diethylamine is also noxious and corrosive. In addition, it is quite volatile (bp 56°C) and must be cooled in a hood prior to use.

PROCEDURE

Apparatus Assembly

Assemble the apparatus shown in Figure 1 in a good fume hood using clean, dry glassware. Omit the gas trap and substitute an addition funnel for the syringe. Use a heating mantle instead of the water bath to avoid any possibility of water vapor coming in contact with thionyl chloride.

Preparation of the Acid Chloride

Place 1.81 g of *m*-toluic acid (3-methylbenzoic acid) into a dry 100-mL round-bottom flask. In a hood, transfer 2.0 mL of thionyl chloride into a test tube with the dry graduated pipet provided with the reagent. Stopper the test tube while bringing it to your hood.

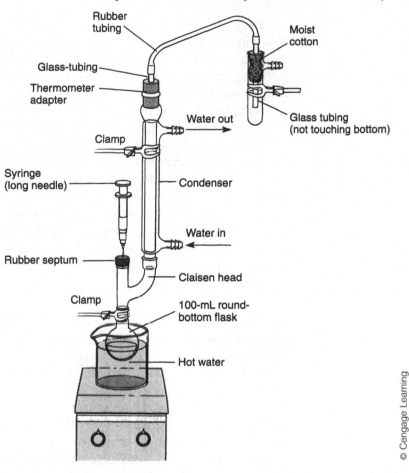

Figure 1
Reflux apparatus.

> **CAUTION**
>
> **The thionyl chloride is kept in a hood. Do not breathe the vapors of this noxious and corrosive chemical. Use dry equipment when handling this material as it reacts violently with water. Do not get it on your skin. If you are using a hot water bath, be sure to remove it from the vicinity of your apparatus so that there is no danger of pouring thionyl chloride into the water.**

Remove the rubber septum and transfer the thionyl chloride into the flask with a Pasteur pipet. Add a boiling stone, reattach the septum, start the circulation of water in the reflux condenser, and gently reflux the mixture for 15 minutes.

Preparation of the Amide   Raise the apparatus from the heating mantle and allow the flask to cool to *room temperature*. Remove the hotplate and heating mantle as the next part of this reaction sequence is conducted at room temperature.

After the mixture has cooled to room temperature, remove the rubber septum and pour 25.0 mL of *anhydrous* ether into the reaction flask. Reattach the septum. While holding the ring stand, swirl the mixture until a homogeneous solution is obtained. In a hood, remove 4.5 mL of ice cold diethylamine and place it in a small Erlenmeyer flask for storage. Add 8 mL of *anhydrous* ether to the amine in the flask.

Pour the diethylamine solution into the addition funnel. Add the solution of diethylamine and ether *dropwise* over a 10–15 minute period to the round-bottom flask. As the solution is added, a voluminous white cloud of diethylamine hydrochloride will form in the flask. Holding the ring stand, swirl the reaction mixture occasionally.

After adding the diethylamine, swirl the mixture occasionally over a 10 minute period. After this time, remove the rubber septum and pour 14 mL of a 10% aqueous sodium hydroxide solution into the flask in small portions. Swirl the contents of the flask occasionally over a 15 minute period. During this time, the sodium hydroxide converts most of the remaining acid chloride to the sodium salt of *m*-toluic acid. This salt is soluble in the aqueous layer. Diethylamine hydrochloride is also water soluble. Any remaining thionyl chloride is destroyed by water present in the aqueous sodium hydroxide. The desired amide is soluble in ether. If any solid remains, you can add water to dissolve it. It may also be helpful to add some ether.

Extraction of Product

Remove the condenser, the addition funnel, and the Claisen head. Transfer all the liquid to a separatory funnel. Shake the funnel vigorously for 2–3 minutes. The shaking operation helps to complete the conversion of any remaining acid chloride to the sodium salt. Allow the layers to separate and then remove the lower aqueous layer, leaving the desired ether layer behind in the separatory funnel. Discard the aqueous layer. Add another 14-mL portion of 10% aqueous sodium hydroxide to the remaining ether layer and again shake the funnel vigorously for 2–3 minutes. Allow the layers to separate, and again remove the lower aqueous layer and discard it.

Now shake the ether layer remaining in the separatory funnel with a 14-mL portion of 10% aqueous hydrochloric acid to remove any remaining diethylamine as its hydrochloride salt. Allow the layers to separate and then drain off the lower aqueous layer and discard it. Finally, shake the ether layer with a 14-mL portion of water and drain off the lower aqueous layer remaining after the layers have separated. Keep the upper ether layer.

Transfer the ether layer containing the amide product to a dry Erlenmeyer flask and dry the ether phase with granular anhydrous sodium sulfate. Decant the ether phase away from the drying agent into another *dry* preweighed flask. Use a small amount of additional ether to rinse the drying agent. Evaporate the ether by placing the flask into a hot water bath at about 50°C, in a good fume hood. A crude dark brown liquid amide will remain. Reweigh the flask to determine the amount of crude product obtained. Column chromatography is used to remove much of the dark color from the product.

Column Chromatography

Preweigh a 100-mL beaker for use in collecting the material eluted from the column. Prepare a column for column chromatography. Place a small piece of cotton into the column and gently push it into the constriction. Pour

7.3 g of alumina[1] into the column while gently tapping the column with a pencil or finger. Obtain about 30 mL of hexane. The hexane will be used to prepare the column, dissolve the crude product, and elute the purified product as described in the next paragraph.

Clamp the column above the preweighed beaker. Then add about 7 mL of hexane to the column and allow it to percolate through the alumina. Allow the solvent to drain until the solvent level just begins to enter the alumina. Dissolve the crude product in about 2 mL of hexane before adding it to the column. Add the solution of crude product and hexane to the top of the column using a Pasteur pipet and allow the mixture to pass onto the column. Use about 4 mL hexane to rinse the flask that contained the crude product. When the first batch of crude product has passed fully into the alumina so that the surface of the liquid just begins to enter the top of the alumina, add the hexane rinse on the column using a pipet.

When the solvent level has again reached the top of the alumina, add more hexane with a pipet to elute the product into the beaker. You should add about 14 mL of hexane, in portions, to the column to elute the product. Collect all of the liquid that passes through the column as one fraction (yellow material). Place the beaker in a warm water bath (about 50°C) and evaporate the hexane with a light stream of air or nitrogen in a hood to give the *N,N*-diethyl-*m*-toluamide as a light tan liquid. If necessary, use a few drops of hexane to rinse the product from the side of the beaker into the bottom. Evaporate this solvent.

Analysis of Product

Reweigh the beaker to determine the weight of product. Calculate the percentage yield of the crude product as well as the column purified product. At the option of your instructor, determine the infrared spectrum of your product (Figure 2).

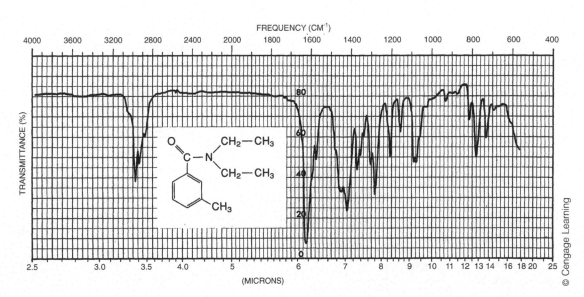

Figure 2
Infrared spectrum (neat) of N,N-*diethyl-*m-*toluamide.*

---

[1]EM Science (No. AX0612-1). The particle sizes are 80–200 mesh and the material is Type F-20.

REFERENCE

Wang, B. J-S. "An Interesting and Successful Organic Experiment." *Journal of Chemical Education*, 51 (October 1974): 632. (The synthesis of *N,N*-diethyl-*m*-toluamide.)

QUESTIONS

1. Write an equation that describes the reaction of thionyl chloride with water.

2. What reaction would take place if the acid chloride of *m*-toluic acid were mixed with water?

3. Why is the reaction mixture extracted with 10% aqueous sodium hydroxide? Write an equation.

4. Write a mechanism for each step in the preparation of *N,N*-diethyl-*m*-toluamide.

5. Interpret each of the principal peaks in the infrared spectrum of *N,N*-diethyl-*m*-toluamide.

6. A student determined the infrared spectrum of the product and found an absorption at 1785 cm^{-1}. The rest of the spectrum resembled the one given in this experiment. Assign this peak and provide an explanation for this unexpected result.

Nitration of Methyl Benzoate

Prepared by Donald L. Pavia, Gary M. Lampman and George S. Kriz, Western Washington University, and Richard Engel, Edmonds Community College

INTRODUCTION

The nitration of methyl benzoate to prepare methyl *m*-nitrobenzoate is an example of an electrophilic aromatic substitution reaction, in which a proton of the aromatic ring is replaced by a nitro group:

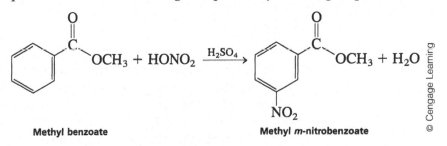

Methyl benzoate   **Methyl *m*-nitrobenzoate**

Many such aromatic substitution reactions are known to occur when an aromatic substrate is allowed to react with a suitable electrophilic reagent, and many other groups besides nitro may be introduced into the ring.

You may recall that alkenes (which are electron-rich due to an excess of electrons in the π system) can react with an electrophilic reagent. The intermediate formed is electron-deficient. It reacts with the nucleophile to complete the reaction. The overall sequence is called **electrophilic addition.** Addition of HX to cyclohexene is an example.

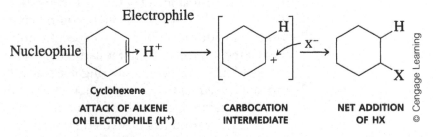

Cyclohexene

| ATTACK OF ALKENE ON ELECTROPHILE (H⁺) | CARBOCATION INTERMEDIATE | NET ADDITION OF HX |

Aromatic compounds are not fundamentally different from cyclohexene. They can also react with electrophiles. However, due to resonance in the ring, the electrons of the π system are generally less available for addition reactions, since an addition would mean the loss of the stabilization that resonance provides. In practice, this means that aromatic compounds react only with *powerfully electrophilic reagents,* usually at somewhat elevated temperatures.

Benzene, for example, can be nitrated at 50°C with a mixture of concentrated nitric and sulfuric acids; the electrophile is NO_2^+ (nitronium ion), whose formation is promoted by action of the concentrated sulfuric acid on nitric acid:

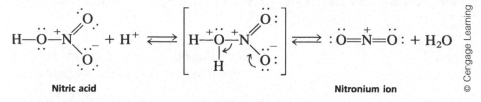

Nitric acid   **Nitronium ion**

The nitronium ion is sufficiently electrophilic to add to the benzene ring, *temporarily* interrupting ring resonance:

The intermediate first formed is somewhat stabilized by resonance and does not rapidly undergo reaction with a nucleophile; in this behavior, it is different from the unstabilized carbocation formed from cyclohexene plus an electrophile. In fact, aromaticity can be restored to the ring if *elimination* occurs instead. (Recall that elimination is often a reaction of carbocations). Removal of a proton, probably by HSO_4^-, from the sp^3-ring carbon *restores the aromatic system* and yields a net *substitution* wherein a hydrogen has been replaced by a nitro group. Many similar reactions are known, and they are called **electrophilic aromatic substitution reactions.**

The substitution of a nitro group for a ring hydrogen occurs with methyl benzoate in the same way as it does with benzene. In principle, one might expect that any hydrogen on the ring could be replaced by a nitro group. However, for reasons beyond our scope here, the carbomethoxy group directs the aromatic substitution preferentially to those positions that are *meta* to it. As a result, methyl *m*-nitrobenzoate is the principal product formed. In addition, one might expect the nitration to occur more than once on the ring. However, both the carbomethoxy group and the nitro group that has just been attached to the ring *deactivate* the ring against further substitution. Consequently, the formation of a methyl dinitrobenzoate product is much less favorable than the formation of the mononitration product.

While the products described previously are the principal ones formed in the reaction, it is possible to obtain as impurities in the reaction small amounts of the ortho and para isomers of methyl *m*-nitrobenzoate and of the dinitration products. These side products are removed when the desired product is washed with methanol and purified by recrystallization.

Water has a retarding effect on the nitration since it interferes with the nitric acid–sulfuric acid equilibria that form the nitronium ions. The smaller the amount of water present, the more active the nitrating mixture. Also, the reactivity of the nitrating mixture can be controlled by varying the amount of sulfuric acid used. This acid must protonate nitric acid, which is a *weak* base, and the larger the amount of acid available, the more numerous the protonated species (and hence NO_2^+) in the solution. Water interferes because it is a stronger base than H_2SO_4 or HNO_3. Temperature is also a factor in determining the extent of nitration. The higher the temperature, the greater will be the amounts of dinitration products formed in the reaction.

SPECIAL INSTRUCTIONS

It is important that the temperature of the reaction mixture be maintained at or below 15°C. Nitric acid and sulfuric acid, especially when mixed, are very corrosive substances. Be careful not to get these acids on your skin. If you do get some of these acids on your skin, flush the affected area liberally with water.

WASTE DISPOSAL

All aqueous solutions should be placed in a container specially designated for aqueous wastes. Place the methanol used to recrystallize the methyl nitrobenzoate in the container designated for nonhalogenated organic waste.

PROCEDURE

In a 150-mL Erlenmeyer flask, cool 12 mL of concentrated sulfuric acid to about 0°C and add 6.1 g of methyl benzoate. Using an ice-salt bath, cool the mixture to 0°C or below and add, VERY SLOWLY, using a Pasteur pipet, a cool mixture of 4 mL of concentrated sulfuric acid and 4 mL of concentrated nitric acid. During the addition of the acids, stir the mixture continuously and maintain the temperature of the reaction below 15°C. If the mixture rises above this temperature, the formation of by-product increases rapidly, bringing about a decrease in the yield of the desired product.

After you have added all the acid, warm the mixture to room temperature. After 15 minutes, pour the acid mixture over 50 g of crushed ice in a 250-mL beaker. After the ice has melted, isolate the product by vacuum filtration through a Büchner funnel and wash it with two 25-mL portions of cold water and then with two 10-mL portions of ice cold methanol. Weigh the product and recrystallize it from an equal weight of methanol. Determine the infrared spectrum of the product as a Nujol mull. (See Figure 1.)

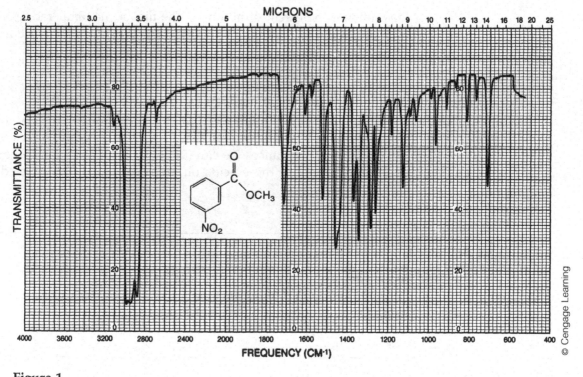

Figure 1
Infrared spectrum of methyl m-*nitrobenzoate, Nujol mull (Nujol peaks: 2850–3000, 1460, and 1380 cm*$^{-1}$*)*

QUESTIONS

1. Why is methyl *m*-nitrobenzoate formed in this reaction instead of the *ortho* or *para* isomers?

2. Why does the amount of dinitration increase at high temperatures?

3. Why is it important to add the nitric acid-sulfuric acid mixture slowly?

4. Interpret the infrared spectrum of methyl *m*-nitrobenzoate.

5. Indicate the major product(s) formed on nitration of each of the following compounds: benzene, toluene, chlorobenzene, and benzoic acid.

1,4-Diphenyl-1,3-Butadiene

Prepared by Donald L. Pavia, Gary M. Lampman and George S. Kriz, Western Washington University, and Richard Engel, Edmonds Community College

INTRODUCTION

The Wittig reaction is often used to form alkenes from carbonyl compounds. In this experiment, the isomeric dienes *cis,trans*, and *trans,trans*-1, 4-diphenyl-1,3-butadiene will be formed from cinnamaldehyde and benzyltriphenylphosphonium chloride Wittig reagent. Only the *trans,trans* isomer will be isolated.

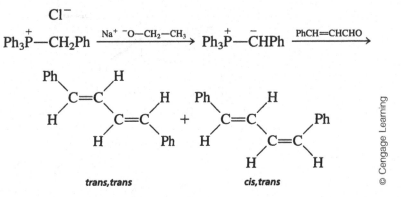

The reaction is carried out in two steps. First, the phosphonium salt is formed by the reaction of triphenylphosphine with benzyl chloride. The reaction is a simple nucleophilic displacement of chloride ion by triphenylphosphine. The salt that is formed is called the "Wittig reagent" or "Wittig salt."

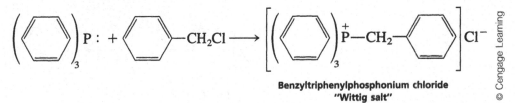

Benzyltriphenylphosphonium chloride
"Wittig salt"

When treated with base, the Wittig salt forms an **ylide.** An ylide is a species having adjacent atoms oppositely charged. The ylide is stabilized due to the ability of phosphorus to accept more than eight electrons in its valence shell. Phosphorus uses its 3d orbitals to form the overlap with the 2p orbital of carbon that is necessary for resonance stabilization. Resonance stabilizes the carbanion.

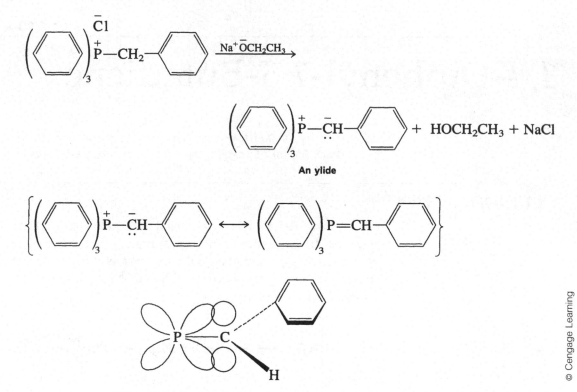

An ylide

The ylide is a carbanion that acts as a nucleophile, and it adds to the carbonyl group in the first step of the mechanism. Following the initial nucleophilic addition, a remarkable sequence of events occurs, as outlined in the following mechanism:

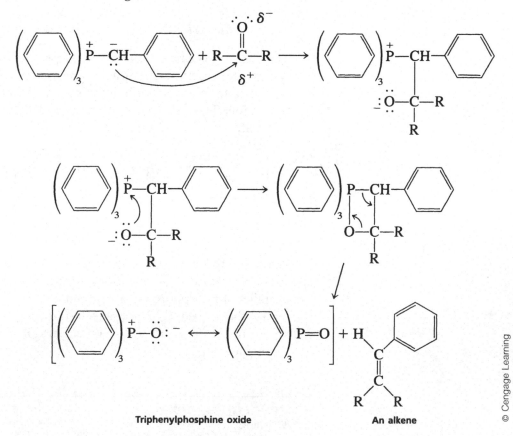

Triphenylphosphine oxide   **An alkene**

The addition intermediate, formed from the ylide and the carbonyl compound, cyclizes to form a four-membered-ring intermediate. This new intermediate is unstable and fragments into an alkene and triphenyl-phosphine oxide. Notice that the ring breaks open in a different way than it was formed. The driving force for this ring opening process is the formation of a very stable substance, triphenylphosphine oxide. A large decrease in potential energy is achieved upon the formation of this thermodynamically stable compound.

In this experiment, cinnamaldehyde is used as the carbonyl compound and yields mainly the *trans,trans-*,1,4-diphenyl-1,3-butadiene which is obtained as a solid. The *cis,trans* isomer is formed in smaller amounts, but it is an oil that is not isolated in this experiment. The *trans,trans* isomer is the more stable isomer and is formed preferentially.

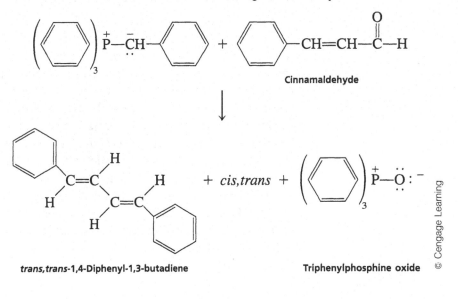

Cinnamaldehyde

trans,trans-1,4-Diphenyl-1,3-butadiene   **Triphenylphosphine oxide**

© Cengage Learning

PROCEDURE

1,4-Diphenyl-1,3-Butadiene

In the following operations, stopper the round-bottom flask whenever possible to avoid contact with moisture from the atmosphere.

Preparation of the Ylide

Place 1.92 g benzyltriphenylphosphonium chloride in a *dry* 50-mL round-bottom flask. Add a magnetic stir bar. Transfer 8.0 mL absolute (anhydrous) ethanol to the flask and stir the mixture to dissolve the phosphonium salt (Wittig salt). Add 3.0 mL of sodium ethoxide solution[1] to the flask using a dry pipet, while stirring continuously. Stopper the flask and stir the mixture for

---

[1] This reagent is prepared in advance by the instructor and will serve about 12 students. Carefully dry a 250-mL Erlenmeyer flask and insert a drying tube filled with calcium chloride into a one-hole rubber stopper. Obtain a large piece of sodium, clean it by cutting off the oxidized surface, weigh out a 2.30-g piece, cut it into 20 smaller pieces, and store it under xylene. Using tweezers remove each piece, wipe off the xylene, and add the sodium slowly over a period of about 30 minutes to 40 mL of absolute (anhydrous) ethanol in the 250-mL Erlenmeyer flask. After the addition of each piece, replace the stopper. The ethanol will warm as the sodium reacts, but do not cool the flask. After the sodium has been added, warm the solution and shake it *gently* until all the sodium reacts. Cool the sodium ethoxide solution to room temperature. This reagent may be prepared in advance of the laboratory period, but it must be stored in a refrigerator between laboratory periods. When it is stored in a refrigerator, it may be kept for about 3 days. Before using this reagent, bring it to room temperature and swirl it gently in order to redissolve any precipitated sodium ethoxide. Keep the flask stoppered between each use.

15 minutes. During this period, the cloudy solution acquires the characteristic yellow color of the ylide.

Reaction of the Ylide with Cinnamaldehyde

Measure 0.60 mL of cinnamaldehyde and place it in a small test tube. To the cinnamaldehyde, add 2.0 mL of absolute ethanol. Stopper the test tube until it is needed. After the 15-minute period, use a Pasteur pipet to mix the cinnamaldehyde with the ethanol and add this solution to the ylide in the round-bottom flask. A color change should be observed as the ylide reacts with the aldehyde and the product precipitates. Stir the mixture for 10 minutes.

Separation of the Isomers of 1,4-Diphenyl-1,3-Butadiene

Cool the flask thoroughly in an ice-water bath, stir the mixture with a spatula, and transfer the material from the flask to a small Büchner funnel under vacuum. Use two 4-mL portions of ice cold absolute ethanol to aid the transfer and to rinse the product. Dry the crystalline *trans,trans*-1,4-diphenyl-1,3-butadiene by drawing air through the solid. The product contains a small amount of sodium chloride that is removed as described in the next paragraph. The cloudy material in the filter flask contains triphenylphosphine oxide, the *cis,trans* isomer, and some *trans,trans* product. Pour the filtrate into a beaker and save it for the thin-layer chromatography experiment described in the next section.

Remove the *trans,trans*-1,4-diphenyl-1,3-butadiene from the filter paper, place the solid in a beaker, and add 12 mL of water. Stir the mixture and filter it on a Büchner funnel, under vacuum, to collect the nearly colorless crystalline *trans,trans* product. Use a minimum of water to aid the transfer. Allow the solid to dry thoroughly.

Analysis of the Filtrate

Use thin-layer chromatography to analyze the filtrate that you saved in the previous section. This mixture must be analyzed as soon as possible so that the *cis,trans* isomer will not be photochemically converted to the *trans,trans* compound. At one position on the TLC plate, spot the filtrate, as is, without dilution. Dissolve a few crystals of the *trans,trans*-1,4-diphenyl-1,3-butadiene in a few drops of acetone and spot it at another position on the plate. Use petroleum ether (bp 60–90°C) as a solvent to develop the plate.

Visualize the spots with a UV lamp using both the long and short wavelength settings. The order of increasing R_f values is as follows: triphenylphosphine oxide, *trans,trans*-diene, *cis,trans*-diene. It is easy to identify the spot for the *trans,trans* isomer because it fluoresces brilliantly. What conclusion can you make about the contents of the filtrate and the purity of the *trans,trans* product? Report the results that you obtain, including R_f values and the appearance of the spots under illumination. Discard the filtrate in the container designated for nonhalogenated waste.

Yield Calculation and Melting Point Determination

When the *trans,trans*-1,4-diphenyl-1,3-butadiene is dry, determine the melting point. Weigh the solid and determine the percentage yield. If the melting point is below 145°C, recrystallize a portion of the compound from hot 95% ethanol. Redetermine the melting point.

Spectroscopy (Optional)

Obtain the proton NMR spectrum in CDCl₃ or the UV spectrum in hexane. For the UV spectrum of the product, dissolve a 10-mg sample in 100 mL of hexane in a volumetric flask. Remove 10 mL of this solution and dilute it to 100 mL in another volumetric flask. This concentration should be adequate for analysis. The *trans,trans* isomer absorbs at 328 nm and possesses fine structure, while the *cis,trans* isomer absorbs at 313 nm and has a smooth curve.[2] See if your spectrum is consistent with these observations. Submit the spectral data with your laboratory report.

QUESTIONS

1. There is an additional isomer of 1,4-diphenyl-1,3-butadiene (mp 70°C), which has not been shown in this experiment. Draw the structure and name it. Why is it not produced in this experiment?

2. Why should the *trans,trans* isomer be the thermodynamically most stable one?

3. A lower yield of phosphonium salt is obtained in refluxing benzene than in xylene. Look up the boiling points for these solvents and explain why the difference in boiling points might influence the yield.

4. Outline a synthesis for *cis* and *trans* stilbene (the 1,2-diphenylethenes) using the Wittig reaction.

5. The sex attractant of the female housefly *(Musca domestica)* is called **muscalure,** and its structure follows. Outline a synthesis of muscalure, using the Wittig reaction. Will your synthesis lead to the required *cis* isomer?

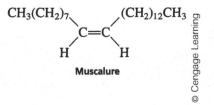

Muscalure

© Cengage Learning

---

[2] The comparative study of the stereoisomeric 1,4-diphenyl-1,3-butadienes has been published: J. H. Pinkard, B. Wille, and L. Zechmeister, *Journal of the American Chemical Society, 70* (1948): 1938.

Coenzyme Synthesis of Benzoin

Prepared by Donald L. Pavia, Gary M. Lampman and George S. Kriz, Western Washington University, and Richard Engel, North Seattle Community College

INTRODUCTION

In this experiment, two molecules of benzaldehyde will be converted to benzoin using the catalyst thiamine hydrochloride. This reaction is known as a benzoin condensation reaction:

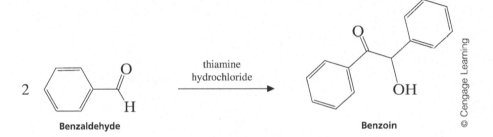

Thiamine hydrochloride is structurally similar to thiamine pyrophosphate (TPP). TPP is a coenzyme universally present in all living systems. It catalyzes several biochemical reactions in natural systems. It was originally discovered as a required nutritional factor (vitamin) in humans by its link with the disease beriberi. **Beriberi** is a disease of the peripheral nervous system caused by a deficiency of Vitamin B_1 in the diet. Symptoms include pain and paralysis of the extremities, emaciation, and swelling of the body. The disease is most common in Asia.

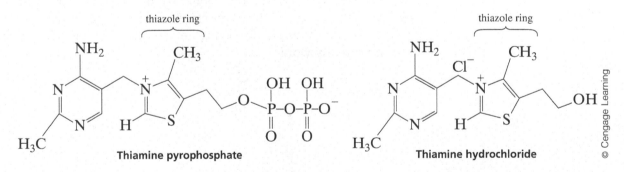

Thiamine binds to an enzyme before the enzyme is activated. The enzyme also binds to the substrate (a large protein). Without the coenzyme thiamine, no chemical reaction would occur. The coenzyme is the **chemical reagent.** The protein molecule (the enzyme) helps and mediates the reaction by controlling stereochemical, energetic, and entropic factors, but it is nonessential to the overall course of reactions that its catalyzes. A special name, vitamins, is given to coenzymes that are essential to the nutrition of the organism.

The most important part of the entire thiamine molecule is the central ring, the thiazole ring, which contains nitrogen and sulfur. This ring constitutes the **reagent** portion of the coenzyme. Experiments with the model compound 3,4-dimethylthiazolium bromide have explained how thiamine-catalyzed reactions work. It was found that this model thiazolium compound rapidly exchanged the C-2 proton for deuterium in D_2O solution. At a pD of 7, this proton was completely exchanged in seconds!

This indicates that the C-2 proton is more acidic than one would have expected. It is apparently easily removed because the conjugate base is a highly stabilized ylide. An **ylide** is a compound or intermediate with positive and negative formal charges on adjacent atoms.

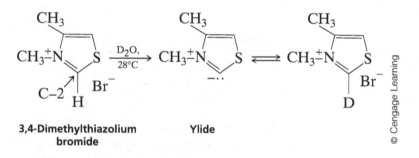

3,4-Dimethylthiazolium　　　　**Ylide**
bromide

The sulfur atom plays an important role in stabilizing this ylide. This was shown by comparing the rate of exchange of 1,3-dimethylimidazolium ion with the rate for the thiazolium compound shown in the previous equation. The dinitrogen compound exchanged its C-2 proton more slowly than the sulfur-containing ion. Sulfur, being in the third row of the periodic chart, has *d* orbitals available for bonding to adjacent atoms. Thus, it has fewer geometrical restrictions than carbon and nitrogen atoms do and can form carbon–sulfur multiple bonds in situations in which carbon and nitrogen normally would not.

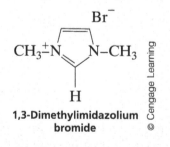

1,3-Dimethylimidazolium
bromide

PROCEDURE

Dissolve 2.0 g of thiamine hydrochloride in about 5 mL of water in a 50-mL round-bottomed flask equipped with a condenser for reflux.

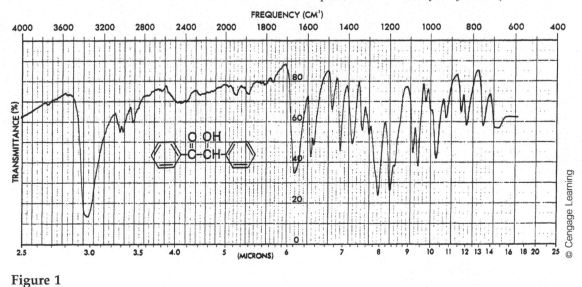

Figure 1
IR spectrum of benzoin (KBr).

Add 15 mL of 95% ethanol and cool the solution by swirling the flask in an ice-water bath. Meanwhile, place about 5 mL of 2*M* sodium hydroxide solution in a small Erlenmeyer flask. Cool this solution in the ice bath also. Then, over about 10 minutes, add the cold sodium hydroxide solution dropwise through the condenser to the thiamine solution. Measure 10 mL of benzaldehyde and add it, also through the condenser, to the reaction mixture. Add a boiling stone and heat the mixture gently on a water bath for about 60 minutes. Do not heat the mixture under vigorous reflux. Allow the mixture to cool to room temperature, and then induce crystallization of the benzoin (it may already have begun) by cooling the mixture in an ice-water bath. If the product separates as an oil, reheat the mixture until it is once again homogeneous, and then allow it to cool more slowly than before. You may have to scratch the flask with a glass rod.

Collect the product by vacuum filtration, using a Büchner funnel. Wash the product with two 25 mL portions of **cold** water. Weigh the crude product and then recrystallize it from 95% ethanol. The solubility of benzoin in boiling 95% ethanol is about 12 to 14 g per 100 mL. Weigh the product, calculate the percentage yield, and determine its melting point.

At your instructor's option, determine the infrared spectrum of the benzoin as a KBr mull. A spectrum of benzoin is shown here for comparison.

QUESTIONS

1. The infrared spectrum of benzoin is given in this experiment. Interpret the principal peaks in the spectrum.

2. Why is sodium hydroxide added to the solution of thiamine hydrochloride?

3. Using the information given in the essay that precedes this experiment, formulate a complete mechanism for the thiamine-catalyzed conversion of benzaldehyde to benzoin.

4. How do you think the appropriate enzyme would have affected the reaction (degree of completion, yield, stereochemistry)?

5. What modifications of conditions would be appropriate if the enzyme were to be used?

6. Refer to the essay that precedes this experiment. It gives a structure for thiamine pyrophosphate. Using this structure as a guide, draw a structure for thiamine hydrochloride. The pyrophosphate group is absent in this compound.

Luminol

Prepared by Donald L. Pavia, Gary M. Lampman and George S. Kriz, Western Washington University, and Richard Engel, Edmonds Community College

INTRODUCTION

In this experiment, the chemiluminescent compound **luminol,** or **5-aminophthalhydrazide,** will be synthesized from 3-nitrophthalic acid.

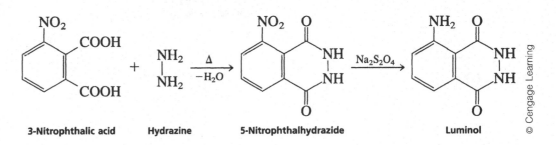

The first step of the synthesis is the simple formation of a cyclic diamide, 5-nitrophthalhydrazide, by reaction of 3-nitrophthalic acid with hydrazine. Reduction of the nitro group with sodium dithionite affords luminol.

In neutral solution, luminol exists largely as a dipolar anion (zwitterion). This dipolar ion exhibits a weak blue fluorescence after being exposed to light. However, in alkaline solution, luminol is converted to its dianion, which may be oxidized by molecular oxygen to give an intermediate that is chemiluminescent. The reaction is thought to have the following sequence:

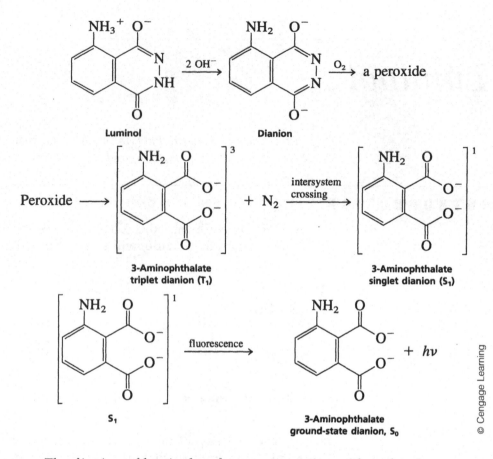

The dianion of luminol undergoes a reaction with molecular oxygen to form a peroxide of unknown structure. This peroxide is unstable and decomposes with the evolution of nitrogen gas, producing the 3-aminophthalate dianion in an electronically excited state. The excited dianion emits a photon that is visible as light. One very attractive hypothesis for the structure of the peroxide postulates a cyclic endoperoxide that decomposes by the following mechanism:

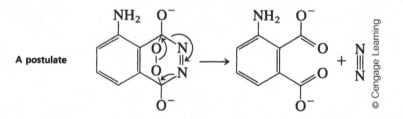

Certain experimental facts argue against this intermediate, however. For instance, certain acyclic hydrazides that cannot form a similar intermediate have also been found to be chemiluminescent.

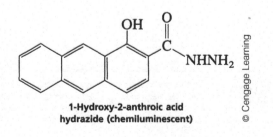

1-Hydroxy-2-anthroic acid hydrazide (chemiluminescent)

Although the nature of the peroxide is still debatable, the remainder of the reaction is well understood. The chemical products of the reaction have been shown to be the 3-aminophthalate dianion and molecular nitrogen. The intermediate that emits light has been identified definitely as the *excited state singlet* of the 3-aminophthalate dianion. Thus, the fluorescence emission spectrum of the 3-aminophthalate dianion (produced by photon absorption) is identical to the spectrum of the light emitted from the chemiluminescent reaction. However, for numerous complicated reasons, it is believed that the 3-aminophthalate dianion is formed first as a vibrationally excited triplet state molecule, which makes the intersystem crossing to the singlet state before emission of a photon.

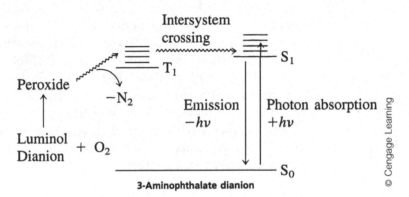

The excited state of the 3-aminophthalate dianion may be quenched by suitable acceptor molecules, or the energy (about 50–80 kcal/mol) may be transferred to give emission from the acceptor molecules. Several such experiments are described in the following procedure.

The system chosen for the chemiluminescence studies of luminol in this experiment uses sodium hydroxide as the base required for the formation of the dianion of luminol, and aqueous potassium ferricyanide (oxidizing agent) with hydrogen peroxide as a substitute for the molecular oxygen.

REFERENCES

Rahaut, M. M. "Chemiluminescence from Concerted Peroxide Decomposition Reactions." *Accounts of Chemical Research*, 2 (1969): 80.

White, E. H., and Roswell, D. F. "The Chemiluminescence of Organic Hydrazides." *Accounts of Chemical Research*, 3 (1970): 54.

SPECIAL INSTRUCTIONS

A darkened room is required to observe adequately the chemiluminescence of luminol. A darkened hood that has had its window covered with butcher paper or aluminum foil also works well. Other fluorescent dyes besides those mentioned (for instance, 9,10-diphenylanthracene) can also be used for the energy-transfer experiments.

PROCEDURE

Part A.
5-Nitrophthalhydrazide

Place 0.60 g of 3-nitrophthalic acid and 0.8 mL of a 10% aqueous solution of hydrazine in a small sidearm test tube.[1] At the same time, heat 8 mL of water in a beaker on a hotplate to about 80°C. Heat the test tube over a Bunsen burner until the solid dissolves. Add 1.6 mL of triethylene glycol and clamp the test tube in an upright position on a ring stand. Place a thermometer (do not seal the system) and a boiling stone in the test tube. Heat the solution with a micro burner until the liquid boils vigorously (the temperature will rise to about 120°C). Continue heating and allow the temperature to increase rapidly until it rises just above 200°C. This heating requires 2–3 minutes, and you must watch the temperature closely to avoid heating the mixture well above 200°C. Remove the burner briefly when this temperature has been achieved and then resume gentle heating to maintain a fairly constant temperature of 220–230°C for about 3 minutes. Allow the test tube to cool to about 100°C, add the 8 mL of hot water that was prepared previously, and cool the test tube to room temperature by allowing tap water to flow over the outside of the test tube. Collect the brown crystals of 5-nitrophthalhydrazide by vacuum filtration, using a small Hirsch funnel. It is not necessary to dry the product before you go on with the next reaction step.

Part B. Luminol
(5-Aminophthalhydrazide)

Transfer the moist 5-nitrophthalhydrazide back into the side-arm test tube. Add 2.6 mL of a 10% sodium hydroxide solution and agitate the mixture until the hydrazide dissolves. Add 1.6 g of sodium dithionite dihydrate (sodium hydrosulfite dihydrate, $Na_2S_2O_4 \cdot 2 H_2O$). Using a Pasteur pipet, add 2–4 mL of water to wash the solid from the walls of the test tube. Add a boiling stone to the test tube. Heat the test tube until the solution boils. Agitate the solution and maintain the boiling, continuing the agitation for at least 5 minutes. Add 1.0 mL of glacial acetic acid and cool the test tube to room temperature by allowing tap water to flow over the outside of it. Agitate the mixture during the cooling step. Collect the light yellow or gold crystals of luminol by vacuum filtration, using a small Hirsch funnel. Save a small sample of this product, allow it to dry overnight, and determine its melting point. The remainder of the luminol may be used without drying for the chemiluminescence experiments. When drying the luminol, it is best to use a vacuum desiccator charged with calcium sulfate drying agent.

Part C. Chemiluminescence Experiments

CAUTION

⚠️

Be careful not to allow any of the mixture to touch your skin while shaking the flask. Hold the stopper securely.

Split luminol evenly into two test tubes and add 1 mL 10% aqueous sodium hydroxide to each tube (Tube A and Tube B). To Tube B, add a tiny amount (1–2 crystals) of the dye of your choice. In a 50 mL beaker, mix 5 mL 3% aqueous hydrogen peroxide, 25 mL water, and a pinch of potassium ferricyanide.

---

[1] A 10% aqueous solution of hydrazine can be prepared by diluting 15.6 g of a commercial 64% hydrazine solution to a volume of 100 mL using water.

Table 1 *Fluorescent dyes and exhibited colors.*

Fluorescent Dye	Color
No dye	Faint bluish white
2,6-Dichloroindophenol	Blue
9-Aminoacridine	Blue-green
Eosin	Salmon pink
Fluorescein	Yellow-green
Dichlorofluorescein	Yellow-orange
Rhodamine B	Pink
Phenolphthalein	Purple

In a dark room, mix half of the hydrogen peroxide solution with the luminol in Tube A and agitate gently. Mix the other half of the hydrogen peroxide solution with the luminol and dye in Test Tube B; agitate gently. Observe the intensity and the color of the light produced.

Table 1 lists some dyes and the colors produced when they are mixed with luminol. Other dyes not included on this list may also be tested in this experiment.

QUESTIONS

1. Write the mechanism for the reaction between 3-nitrophthalic acid and hydrazine to form 5-nitrophthalhydrazide.

2. Why is it relatively easy to deprotonate (the nitrogen in the ring) luminol upon addition of sodium hydroxide?

p-Aminobenzoic Acid

Prepared by Donald L. Pavia, Gary M. Lampman and George S. Kriz, Western Washington University, and Richard Engel, Edmonds Community College

INTRODUCTION

The object of this set of chemical reactions is to prepare the vitamin (for bacteria) *p*-aminobenzoic acid, or PABA. For a description of the importance of PABA in biological processes, refer to the Introduction of the Sulfa Drugs experiment. Because PABA can absorb the ultraviolet component of solar radiation, it also finds an important application in sunscreen preparations.

The synthesis of *p*-aminobenzoic acid involves three reactions, which are outlined in the following paragraphs. The first of these reactions is the conversion of the commercially available *p*-toluidine into *N*-acetyl-*p*-toluidine (or *p*-acetotoluidide), the corresponding amide. The reaction is carried out by treating the amine, *p*-toluidine, with acetic anhydride. Such a procedure is a standard method for preparing amides. The reason for acetylating the amine in the initial step is to protect it during the second step, a permanganate oxidation. If the oxidation of the methyl group to the corresponding carboxyl group were carried out directly with *p*-toluidine, the highly reactive amino group would also be oxidized in the reaction. To prevent this undesired oxidation, a protective group is used. A protective group is a functional group that is added during a reaction sequence to shield a particular position on a molecule from undesired reactions. A good protective group is one that is easily added to the substrate molecule,

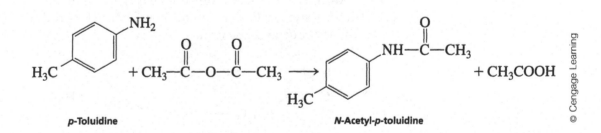

p-Toluidine   *N*-Acetyl-*p*-toluidine

does not permit the protected group to undergo reactions, and is easily removed after the protective role has been played. This last point is important, since if the protective group cannot be removed, the original functional group cannot be used. In the example used in this experiment, the protective group is the acetyl group. The amide formed in this initial reaction is stable toward the oxidation conditions used in the second step. As a result, the methyl group can be oxidized without destroying the amino function in the process.

The second step of this reaction sequence is the oxidation of the methyl group to the corresponding carboxyl group, with potassium permanganate serving as the oxidizing agent. Because of the great stability of substituted benzoic acids, alkyl groups

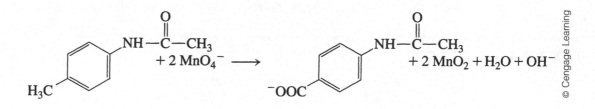

attached to aromatic rings can be oxidized easily to the corresponding benzoic acids. During the oxidation, the violet solution of permanganate ion is converted to a brown precipitate, manganese dioxide, as Mn(VII) is reduced to Mn(IV). The product of the reaction is not the carboxylic acid but rather its salt that is produced directly from the reaction. Acidification of the reaction mixture yields the carboxylic acid, which precipitates from solution.

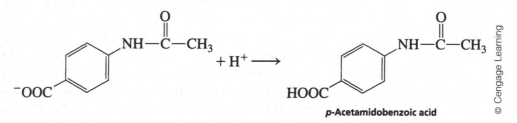

p-Acetamidobenzoic acid

The final step of this procedure is the hydrolysis of the amide functional group to remove the protecting acetyl group; *p*-aminobenzoic acid is thus produced. The reaction proceeds easily in dilute aqueous acid, and it is a characteristic reaction of amides in general. The product is crystallized from dilute aqueous acetic acid.

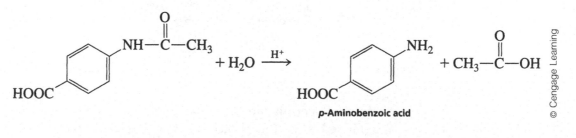

p-Aminobenzoic acid

SPECIAL INSTRUCTIONS

This experiment should be conducted in two parts. It is essential that the procedure be carried out through placing the crystals of *p*-acetamidobenzoic acid in the drying oven in the first laboratory period. Between 1 and 1.5 hours of reaction time are needed to reach this point, along with considerable time spent on other operations.

p-Toluidine is toxic and is suspected to be a carcinogen. Do not allow it to come in contact with your skin. Wear protective gloves and open the bottle in the hood.

WASTE DISPOSAL

Dispose of any organic materials in the waste container specified for nonhalogenated organic waste. Dispose of any aqueous solutions in the waste container designated for the disposal of aqueous waste. Dispose of solid inorganic materials in the container identified for the disposal of inorganic solids.

PROCEDURE

N-Acetyl-*p*-Toluidine

Place 0.80 g of powdered p-toluidine in a 50-mL Erlenmeyer flask. Add 20 mL of water and 0.8 mL of concentrated hydrochloric acid. Warm the mixture in a water bath on a hotplate, with stirring, to facilitate solution. If the solution is dark, add a small amount of decolorizing charcoal (Norit), stir it for several minutes, and filter by gravity through fluted filter paper.

Prepare a solution of 0.72 g sodium acetate in 2 mL of water. If necessary, use a steam bath or a hotplate to warm the solution until all the solid has dissolved.

Warm the decolorized solution of p-toluidine hydrochloride to 50°C. Add 0.85 mL of acetic anhydride, stir rapidly, and immediately add the previously prepared sodium acetate solution. Mix the solution thoroughly, and cool the mixture in an ice bath. A white solid should appear at this point. Filter the mixture by vacuum, using a Büchner funnel, wash the crystals three times with cold water, and allow the crystals to stand in the filter to air-dry while the vacuum is maintained. These crystals will not be isolated and dried but will be used directly in the next step.

p-Acetamidobenzoic Acid

Place the previously prepared, wet N-acetyl-p-toluidine in a 100-mL round-bottom flask, along with 1.4 g of potassium permanganate and 30 mL of water. Add a stir bar to the flask, and attach a reflux condenser. Heat the solution to boiling with vigorous stirring. Use a heating mantle with a magnetic stirrer or a large sand bath on a hotplate/stirrer to heat the solution. Throughout the reaction, pay careful attention to ensure that the reaction mixture does not boil too vigorously. If frothing occurs, it may force the mixture into the condenser.

After 20 minutes of heating, the pink color should have disappeared and the reaction mixture should appear brown. Remove the apparatus from the heat and allow it to cool for a few minutes. Add an additional 1.4 g of potassium permanganate to the flask, and heat the mixture again under reflux, with stirring, for another 20 minutes, or until no pink color remains.

Vacuum filter the *hot* solution through a bed of Celite. Wash the precipitated manganese dioxide with a small amount of hot water. If the filtrate shows the presence of excess permanganate by its pink color, add *not more than* 0.10 mL of ethanol, heat the solution under reflux for another 10 minutes, and filter the *hot* solution through fluted filter paper. Cool the pale yellow filtrate and acidify with excess 20% sulfuric acid solution. A white solid should form at this point. Filter the solid by vacuum filtration and dry it in an oven. The yield based on *p*-toluidine and the melting point should now be determined. The melting point of the pure material is 255 to 262°C. In some cases an inorganic salt may be produced. If a salt is produced, simply go to the next step of the procedure.

p-Aminobenzoic Acid

Prepare a dilute solution of hydrochloric acid by mixing 2.4 mL of concentrated hydrochloric acid and 2.4 mL of water. Place the previously prepared *p*-acetamidobenzoic acid and boiling stones in a 25-mL round-bottom flask that has a reflux condenser attached to it. Add the hydrochloric acid solution. Heat the mixture gently under reflux for 30 minutes. Allow the reaction mixture to cool, transfer it to a 50-mL Erlenmeyer flask, add 1.5 mL of water, and make the solution just alkaline (pH 8–9; use pH paper) by adding concentrated ammonium hydroxide dropwise. For each 3 mL of final solution, add 0.5 mL of glacial acetic acid, chill the solution in an ice bath, and initiate crystallization by scratching the inside of the flask with a glass rod. Filter the crystals by vacuum on a Hirsch funnel and allow them to dry.

Determine the yield for this step, basing the overall yield on *p*-toluidine. Determine the melting point of the product. Frequently, the melting point of the product is somewhat lower than the literature value. Attempts to recrystallize the product are not sufficiently promising to be recommended. At the option of the instructor, an infrared spectrum of the *p*-aminobenzoic acid may be determined. (See Figure 1.)

Save the *p*-aminobenzoic acid for use in the preparation of benzocaine.

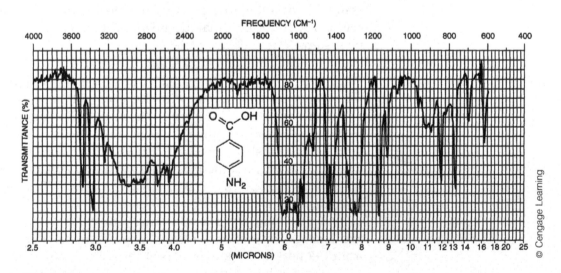

Figure 1
IR spectrum of p-aminobenzoic acid (KBr).

© Cengage Learning

REFERENCE

Kremer, C. B. "The Laboratory Preparation of a Simple Vitamin: *p-*Aminobenzoic Acid." *Journal of Chemical Education*, 33 (1956): 71.

QUESTIONS

1. Write a mechanism for the reaction of *p*-toluidine with acetic anhydride. Why is sodium acetate added to this reaction?

2. In the oxidation step, if excess permanganate remains after the reaction period, a small amount of ethanol is added to discharge the purple color. Write a chemical equation that describes the reaction of permanganate with ethanol.

3. Write a mechanism for the acid-catalyzed hydrolysis of *p*-acetamidobenzoic acid to form *p*-aminobenzoic acid.

4. Interpret the principal absorption bands in the infrared spectrum of *p*-aminobenzoic acid.

Benzocaine

Prepared by Donald L. Pavia, Gary M. Lampman and George S. Kriz, Western Washington University, and Richard Engel, Edmonds Community College

INTRODUCTION

Local anesthetics, or "painkillers," are a well-studied class of compounds with which chemists have shown their ability to study the essential features of a naturally occurring drug and to improve on them by substituting totally new, synthetic surrogates. Often such substitutes are superior in desired medical effects and in lack of unwanted side effects or hazards.

The coca shrub *(Erythroxylon coca)* grows wild in Peru, specifically in the Andes Mountains, at elevations of 1,500 to 6,000 ft above sea level. The natives of South America have long chewed these leaves for their stimulant effects. Leaves of the coca shrub have even been found in pre-Inca Peruvian burial urns. The leaves bring about a definite sense of mental and physical well-being and have the power to increase endurance. For chewing,

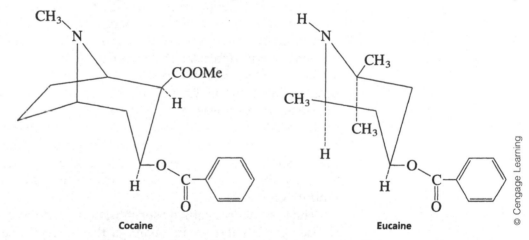

Cocaine   **Eucaine**

the Indians smear the coca leaves with lime and roll them. The lime $Ca(OH)_2$ apparently releases the free alkaloid components; it is remarkable that the Indians learned this subtlety long ago by some empirical means. The pure alkaloid responsible for the properties of the coca leaves is **cocaine.**

The amounts of cocaine consumed in this way by the Indians are extremely small. Without such a crutch of central-nervous-system stimulation, the natives of the Andes would probably find it more difficult to perform the nearly Herculean tasks of their daily lives, such as carrying heavy loads over the rugged mountainous terrain. Unfortunately, overindulgence in cocaine can lead to mental and physical deterioration and eventually an unpleasant death.

The pure alkaloid in large quantities is a common drug of addiction. Sigmund Freud first made a detailed study of cocaine in 1884. He was particularly impressed by the ability of the drug to stimulate the central nervous system, and he used it as a replacement drug to wean one of his addicted colleagues from morphine. This attempt was successful, but unhappily, the colleague became the world's first known cocaine addict.

An extract from coca leaves was one of the original ingredients in Coca-Cola. However, early in the present century, government officials, with much legal difficulty, forced the manufacturer to omit coca from its beverage. The company has managed to this day to maintain the *coca* in its trademarked title even though "Coke" contains none.

Our interest in cocaine lies in its anesthetic properties. The pure alkaloid was isolated in 1862 by Niemann, who noted that it had a bitter taste and produced a queer numbing sensation on the tongue, rendering it almost devoid of sensation. (Oh, those brave, but foolish chemists of yore who used to taste everything!) In 1880, Von Anrep found that the skin was made numb and insensitive to the prick of a pin when cocaine was injected sub-cutaneously. Freud and his assistant Karl Koller, having failed at attempts to rehabilitate morphine addicts, turned to a study of the anesthetizing properties of cocaine. Eye surgery is made difficult by involuntary reflex movements of the eye in response to even the slightest touch. Koller found that a few drops of a solution of cocaine would overcome this problem. Not only can cocaine serve as a local anesthetic, but it can also be used to produce **mydriasis** (dilation of the pupil). The ability of cocaine to block signal conduction in nerves (particularly of pain) led to its rapid medical use in spite of its dangers. It soon found use as a "local" in both dentistry (1884) and in surgery (1885). In this type of application, it was injected directly into the particular nerves it was intended to deaden.

Soon after the structure of cocaine was established, chemists began to search for a substitute. Cocaine has several drawbacks for wide medical use as an anesthetic. In eye surgery it also produces mydriasis; it can become a drug of addiction; and finally, it has a dangerous effect on the central nervous system.

The first totally synthetic substitute was eucaine. It was synthesized by Harries in 1918 and retains many of the essential skeletal features of the cocaine molecule. The development of this new anesthetic partly confirmed the portion of the cocaine structure essential for local anesthetic action. The advantage of eucaine over cocaine is that it does not produce mydriasis and is not habit-forming. Unfortunately, it is highly toxic.

A further attempt at simplification led to piperocaine. The molecular portion common to cocaine and eucaine is outlined by dotted lines in the structure shown. Piperocaine is only a third as toxic as cocaine itself.

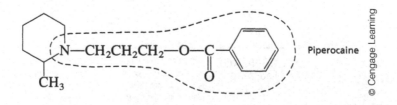

Piperocaine

© Cengage Learning

Local anesthetics

Aromatic residue	Intermediate chain	Amino group	
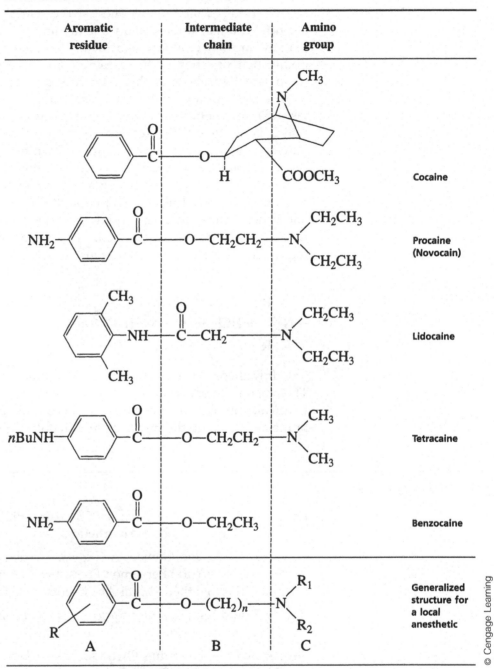			Cocaine
			Procaine (Novocain)
			Lidocaine
			Tetracaine
			Benzocaine
A	B	C	Generalized structure for a local anesthetic

The most successful synthetic for many years was the drug procaine, known more commonly by its trade name Novocain (see table). Novocain is only a fourth as toxic as cocaine, giving a better margin of safety in its use. The toxic dose is almost ten times the effective amount, and it is not a habit-forming drug.

Over the years, hundreds of new local anesthetics have been synthesized and tested. For one reason or another, most have not come into general use. The search for the perfect local anesthetic is still under way.

All the drugs found to be active have certain structural features in common. At one end of the molecule is an aromatic ring. At the other is a secondary or tertiary amine. These two essential features are separated by a central chain of atoms usually one to four units long. The aromatic part is usually an ester of an aromatic acid. The ester group is important to the bodily detoxification of these compounds. The first step in deactivating them is a hydrolysis of this ester linkage, a process that occurs in the bloodstream. Compounds that do not have the ester link are both longer lasting in their effects and generally more toxic. An exception is lidocaine, which is an amide. The tertiary amino group is apparently necessary to enhance the solubility of the compounds in the injection solvent. Most of these compounds are used in their hydrochloride salt forms, which can be dissolved in water for injection. Benzocaine, in contrast, is active as a local anesthetic but is not used for injection. It does not suffuse well into tissue and is not water-soluble. It is used primarily in skin preparations, in which it can be included in an ointment or salve for direct application. It is an ingredient of many sunburn preparations.

$$-\overset{\displaystyle R}{\underset{\displaystyle R}{\ddot{N}}} \; + \; HCl \; \longrightarrow \; -\overset{\displaystyle R}{\underset{\displaystyle R}{N}}{}^{\oplus}\!-H \; \; Cl^{\ominus}$$

© Cengage Learning

How these drugs act to stop pain conduction is not well understood. Their main site of action is at the nerve membrane. They seem to compete with calcium at some receptor site, altering the permeability of the membrane and keeping the nerve slightly depolarized electrically.

REFERENCES

Foye, W. O. *Principles of Medicinal Chemistry*. Philadelphia: Lea & Febiger, 1974. Chap. 14, "Local Anesthetics."

Goodman, L. S., and Gilman, A. *The Pharmacological Basis of Therapeutics*. 8th ed. New York: Pergamon Press, 1990. Chap. 15, "Cocaine, Procaine and Other Synthetic Local Anesthetics," by J. M. Ritchie, et al.

Ray, O. S. and Ksir, C. *Drugs, Society, and Human Behavior*. 7th ed. St. Louis: C. V. Mosby, 1996, Chap. 7, "Stimulants."

Snyder, S. H. "The Brain's Own Opiates." *Chemical and Engineering News* (November 28, 1977): 26–35.

Taylor, N. *Narcotics: Nature's Dangerous Gifts*. New York: Dell, 1970. Paperbound revision of *Flight from Reality*. Chap. 3, "The Divine Plant of the Incas."

Taylor, N. *Plant Drugs That Changed the World*. New York: Dodd, Mead, 1965. Pp. 14–18.

Wilson, C. O., Gisvold, O., and Doerge, R. F. *Textbook of Organic Medicinal and Pharmaceutical Chemistry*. 6th ed. Philadelphia: J. B. Lippincott, 1971. Chap. 22, "Local Anesthetic Agents," R. F. Doerge.

EXPERIMENT

Esterification

In this experiment, a procedure is given for the preparation of a local anesthetic, benzocaine, by the direct esterification of *p*-aminobenzoic acid with ethanol. At the instructor's option, you may test the prepared anesthetic on a frog's leg muscle.

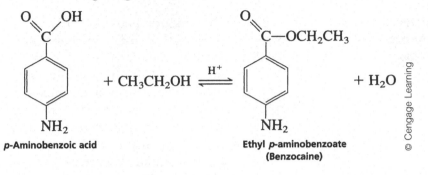

© Cengage Learning

SPECIAL INSTRUCTIONS

Sulfuric acid is very corrosive. Do not allow it to come in contact with your skin. Use a calibrated Pasteur pipet to transfer the liquid.

PROCEDURE

Running the Reaction

Place 1.2 g of *p*-aminobenzoic acid and 12 mL of absolute ethanol in a 100-mL round-bottom flask. Swirl the mixture until the solid dissolves completely. While gently swirling, add dropwise 1.0 mL of concentrated sulfuric acid from a calibrated Pasteur pipet. A large amount of precipitate forms when you add the sulfuric acid, but this solid will slowly dissolve during the reflux that follows. Add boiling stones to the flask, attach a reflux condenser, and heat the mixture at a gentle reflux for 60–75 minutes using a heating mantle. Occasionally swirl the reaction mixture during this period to help avoid bumping.

Precipitation of Benzocaine

At the end of the reaction time, remove the apparatus from the heating mantle and allow the reaction mixture to cool for several minutes. Using a Pasteur pipet, transfer the contents of the flask to a beaker containing 30 mL of water. When the liquid has cooled to room temperature, add aqueous saturated sodium carbonate dropwise to neutralize the mixture. Stir the contents of the beaker with a stirring rod or spatula. After each addition of the sodium carbonate solution, extensive gas evolution (frothing) will be noticeable until the mixture is nearly neutralized. As the pH increases, a white precipitate of benzocaine is produced. When gas no longer evolves as you add a drop of sodium carbonate, check the pH of the solution and add further portions of sodium carbonate until the pH is about 8.

Collect the benzocaine by vacuum filtration using a Büchner funnel. Use three 10-mL portions of water to aid in the transfer and to wash the product in the funnel. Be sure that the solid is rinsed thoroughly with water so that any sodium sulfate formed during the neutralization will be washed out of your product. After the product has dried overnight, weigh it, calculate the percentage yield, and determine its melting point.

Recrystallization and Characterization of Benzocaine

Although the product should be fairly pure, it may be recrystallized by the mixed solvent method using methanol and water. Place the product in a small Erlenmeyer flask and add hot methanol until the solid dissolves; swirl the mixture to help dissolve the solid. After the solid has dissolved, add hot water dropwise until the mixture turns cloudy or a white precipitate forms. Add a few more drops of hot methanol until the solid or oil redissolves completely. Allow the solution to cool slowly to room temperature. Scratch the inside of the flask as the contents cool to help crystallize the benzocaine; otherwise an oil may form. Complete the crystallization by cooling the mixture in an ice bath and collect the crystals by vacuum filtration. Use a minimum amount of ice cold methanol to aid the transfer of the solid from the flask to the filter. When the benzocaine is thoroughly dry, weigh the purified benzocaine. Again, calculate the percentage yield of benzocaine and determine its melting point.

At the option of the instructor, obtain the infrared spectrum in chloroform and the NMR spectrum in $CDCl_3$. Submit the sample in a labeled vial to the instructor.

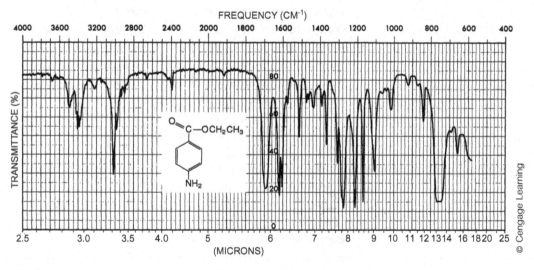

Figure 1
IR spectrum of benzocaine (CHCl$_3$). (CHCl$_3$ solvent: 3030, 1220, and 750 cm^{-1})

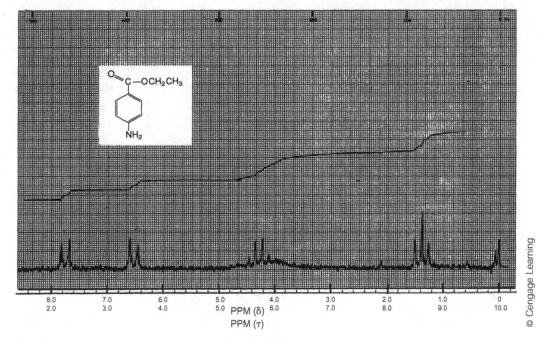

Figure 2
NMR spectrum of benzocaine (in CCl₄).

QUESTIONS

1. Interpret the infrared and NMR spectra of benzocaine (Figures 1 and 2).

2. What is the structure of the precipitate that forms after the sulfuric acid has been added?

3. When 10% sodium carbonate solution is added, a gas evolves. What is the gas? Give a balanced equation for this reaction.

4. Explain why benzocaine precipitates during the neutralization.

5. Refer to the structure of procaine in the table in the essay "Local Anesthetics." Using *p*-aminobenzoic acid, give equations showing how procaine and procaine monohydrochloride could be prepared. Which of the two possible amino functional groups in procaine will be protonated first? Defend your choice. (*Hint:* Consider resonance.)

Addition of Grignard Reagents to Chiral Ketones

Prepared by Donald L. Pavia, Gary M. Lampman and George S. Kriz, Western Washington University, and Richard Engel, Edmonds Community College; and the Sibi Group, North Dakota State University

TRIPHENYLMETHANOL AND BENZOIC ACID

In this experiment, you will prepare a Grignard reagent, or organo-magnesium reagent. The reagent is phenylmagnesium bromide.

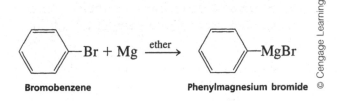

This reagent will be converted to a tertiary alcohol or a carboxylic acid, depending on the experiment selected.

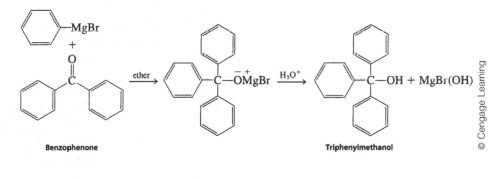

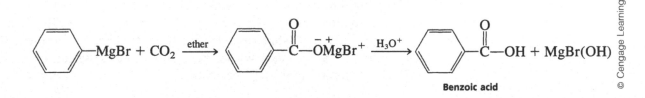

The alkyl portion of the Grignard reagent behaves as if it had the characteristics of a **carbanion.** We may write the structure of the reagent as a partially ionic compound:

$$\overset{\delta-}{R}\cdots\overset{\delta+}{MgX}$$

This partially bonded carbanion is a Lewis base. It reacts with strong acids, as you would expect, to give an alkane:

$$\overset{\delta-}{R}\cdots\overset{\delta+}{MgX} + HX \longrightarrow R-H + MgX_2$$

Any compound with a suitably acidic hydrogen will donate a proton to destroy the reagent. Water, alcohols, terminal acetylenes, phenols, and carboxylic acids are all acidic enough to bring about this reaction.

The Grignard reagent also functions as a good nucleophile in nucleophilic addition reactions of the carbonyl group. The carbonyl group has electrophilic character at its carbon atom (due to resonance), and a good nucleophile seeks out this center for addition.

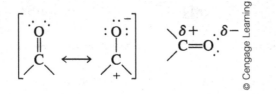

© Cengage Learning

The magnesium salts produced form a complex with the addition product, an alkoxide salt. In a second step of the reaction, these must be hydrolyzed (protonated) by addition of dilute aqueous acid:

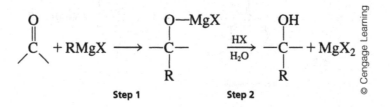

Step 1   **Step 2**

© Cengage Learning

The Grignard reaction is used synthetically to prepare secondary alcohols from aldehydes and tertiary alcohols from ketones. The Grignard reagent will react with esters twice to give tertiary alcohols. Synthetically, it also can be allowed to react with carbon dioxide to give carboxylic acids and with oxygen to give hydroperoxides:

$$RMgX + O=C=O \longrightarrow R-\overset{O}{\overset{\|}{C}}-OMgX \xrightarrow[H_2O]{HX} R-\overset{O}{\overset{\|}{C}}-OH$$

Carboxylic acid

$$RMgX + O_2 \longrightarrow ROOMgX \xrightarrow[H_2O]{HX} ROOH$$

Hydroperoxide

© Cengage Learning

Because the Grignard reagent reacts with water, carbon dioxide, and oxygen, it must be protected from air and moisture when it is used. The apparatus in which the reaction is to be conducted must be scrupulously dry (recall that 18 mL of H_2O is 1 mole), and the solvent must be free of water, or anhydrous. During the reaction, the flask must be protected by a calcium chloride drying tube. Oxygen should also be excluded. In practice this can be done by allowing the solvent ether to reflux. This blanket of solvent vapor keeps air from the surface of the reaction mixture.

In the experiment described here, the principal impurity is **biphenyl**, which is formed by a heat- or light-catalyzed coupling reaction of the Grignard reagent and unreacted bromobenzene. A high reaction temperature favors the formation of this product. Biphenyl is highly soluble in petroleum ether, and it is easily separated from triphenylmethanol. Biphenyl can be separated from benzoic acid by extraction.

EXPERIMENTAL SCHEME

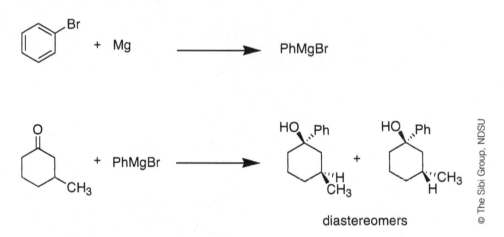

diastereomers

© The Sibi Group, NDSU

Procedure

Prepare two drying tubes using cotton and calcium chloride to use on top of the condenser and the addition funnel. In a dry 3-neck 100 mL round bottom flask equipped with a reflux condenser and a stir bar, add 5 mL dry diethyl ether to 0.5 g Mg turnings. Add 1 crystal of I_2. In a separate Erlenmeyer flask, make a solution of 2.3 mL of bromobenzene in 10 mL dry ether. Add this solution via addition funnel slowly, <u>dropwise</u> to the Mg (make sure the Mg in ether is stirring during the entire time). The reaction is initiated when the yellow color disappears. The formation of the Grignard reagent produces a lot of heat which will cause the ether to reflux. This refluxing should not be too vigorous or else a lot of by-products will form. If this happens, the outside of the flask can be cooled with cold water. After all of the bromobenzene solution has been added, let the reaction mixture stir ~15 minutes. Most of the Mg should be dissolved at this point (if not, reflux may be required). Make up a separate solution of 2.1 mL 3-methylcyclohexanone in 10 mL dry ether and add this solution slowly, dropwise via addition funnel to the reaction mixture. After the addition is complete, let the reaction mixture stir for ~30 minutes.

Work Up

The product is hydrolyzed by adding ice, then 10 mL NH_4Cl (10% aqueous). Separate the ether layer and extract with 15 mL $NaHCO_3$. Dry the organic layer with Na_2SO_4, filter and concentrate on the rotary evaporator. Measure the mass of the product. HPLC analysis of the product should reveal 2 diastereomers.

High-Performance Liquid Chromatography (HPLC) Analysis of 1-Phenyl-3-Methylcyclohexanols

Prepared by Dr. Gary Stolzenberg, North Dakota State University

INTRODUCTION

As with gas chromatography (GC or GLC; recall your work with isoamyl acetate), liquid chromatography, especially High Performance Liquid Chromatography (HPLC), can separate many components(even > 35). HPLC results often are reported as retention times (in minutes or recorder chart distance), similar to GC. You will apply simple isocratic (constant solvent composition) HPLC to analyze your synthetic product.

The column used is filled with a conventional polar stationary phase like silica gel ("normal-phase" HPLC). You will not use a reversed-phase packing of finely-divided silica that has been derivatized with covalently-bonded alkyl groups making the stationary phase non-polor or lipophilic ("oil loving"). These retain (absorb) organic compounds largely in proportion to hydrocarbon content, and retention is decreased (or, mobility is increased) by polar substituents such as hydroxyls, carboxyls, carbonyls, amines, etc.

A typical HPLC system (see your text!) has some pre-column components: the solvent pump and a sample injector. The solvent/sample mixture enters a column for separation through the injector and the mobile phase is pumped through the column. The usual post-column HPLC component is some type of detector, often one measuring light absorption in the near-ultraviolet (typically at 254 or 280 nanometers). Samples with aromatic rings or carbonyl groups strongly absorb these wavelengths; thus, solvents like benzene, toluene or acetone cannot be used. In RP-HPLC the solvent often is a mixture of water (highly purified, possibly with some buffer or salt) and methanol (or the more costly acetonitrile). These are "transparent" at the wavelengths of interest and do not interfere with detection of the samples. Similarly, for normal-phase separations, we will use hexane + isopropyl alcohol.

HPLC techniques are applied extensively and routinely in biological and chemical analyses. Because clinical laboratories and medical researchers often use water-based samples (blood serum, culture broth, urine), RP-HPLC procedures may be the method of choice. Such samples often undergo a preliminary clean-up and pre-concentration by a related RP technique, solid-phase extraction (SPE): the aqueous sample is passed through a filter or "bed" with a C18 or similar RP coating which strongly retains many organics; this bed is washed with water to remove peptides, buffer salts, sugars, etc. Then the biochemical or pharmacological components of interest are eluted rapidly (without any separation) with a small volume of (usually 100%) methanol, etc.

Add one drop of your sample to a 1 dram vial and dilute with hexane. In this analysis you will use a silica gel based column (4.6 mm id, 250 mm length). The solvent is Hexane:Isopropanol (v/v) 95:5 @1.6 mL/min.

Retention Times (Approximate):

Biphenyl	2.0 min
Diastereomer 1	2.3 min
Diastereomer 2	2.8 min
3-Methylcyclohexanone	4.0 min

QUESTIONS

1. Grignard reagents must be kept away from air and moisture. Write chemical equations showing how a generic Grignard (RMgX) reacts with CO_2 and O_2.

2. Provide methods for preparing the following by Grignard method.

   a. 3-pentanol

   b. 3-methyl-3-pentanol